SAILING SOLO ALONE

By

J.J. James

Sailing Solo Alone

J.J. James

Published by J.J. James at AMJ Publishing

Copyright © J.J. James 2011

ISBN 978-0-9569219-0-1 (Paperback)

ISBN 978-0-9569219-1-8 (E-book)

Contents

SAILING SOLO ALONE   1

Acknowledgements   4

Introduction   6

Chapter One -The Boat of Your Dreams   13

Chapter Two -A Little History   36

Chapter Three -Teach Yourself Yachting   78

Chapter Four -The First Leg   111

Chapter Five -Shore Leave   155

Chapter Six -The Second Leg   171

Chapter Seven -The Homeward Leg   211

Chapter Eight -The Final Chapter   261

Chapter Nine -The Last Bit   274

Review   276

Acknowledgements

With grateful thanks in making this book
to:

Bill Bennett

Peter Adams

Danny Horne

Also, I should mention my long-suffering

Wife

Lynn

THIS BOOK IS WRITTEN FOR ALL THOSE

FOOLISH ENOUGH NOT TO GIVE THE SEA

THE RESPECT SHE DESERVES

Introduction

On the face of it, even looking back, floating around on the ocean waves was the ideal career for me, or at the very least, the ideal hobby. After all, I loved boats and the sea, all things nautical in fact. There was only one slight fly in the bilges. Boats didn't love me and if the truth were known, the sea wasn't too keen on me either.

The sad fact of the matter seemed to be, put me near floating objects and disaster would ensue. You can't really count changing the light bulb in the bath, technically I wasn't floating, frothed a bit, but definitely no floating.

Most people, when they try something new and it nearly kills them. They will no doubt have a little think to themselves and probably decide it would be a good idea not to do that again. If they happen to be foolhardy enough to try this sport, or whatever it might be, for a second time and the result, once more, a near death experience. Normal people say to themselves: 'Nearly got killed there... Again! Think it might be better if I never have anything to do with that... Ever Again!!!'

And my reaction? 'Oops! Worse things happen at sea.' If you are in the middle of the sea at the time, all you are left with is the 'Oops!' Doesn't really cut it somehow. You've accidentally pressed the wrong button on the nuclear power plant consul... 'Oops!' Surely there should be more of a reaction than that? You wouldn't want a nuclear reaction obviously, just something with a bit more oomph.

Of course, this was all due to my devil may care attitude; my quest for thrills and excitement; my deep desire to live life to the full. Eh! No... What we are actually talking about here is insanity, a benign, snowball in your face kind of insanity, but insanity nevertheless.

Just to compound this insanity, there I was, sat in front of my computer, punching 'Motor Cruisers' into the search engine. A Bayliner motor cruiser no less, 35 knots plus. When you take into account the fly-water business, coupled with the speed of one of these slick vessels, put it like this: let loose with a machine like that, I could do a lot of damage and worryingly, most of it to myself.

The question had to be asked. Why did I keep going back for more? Was there something wrong with me? Did I have some kind of a death wish? It kind of made you wonder.

It *did* make me wonder and as I sat there, with these thoughts reverberating around my brain, trying to make sense of it all. Suddenly it came to me... I should write a book.

Writing a book would not only help me understand this obsession I appeared to be stuck with, but at the same time, I could pass on all this hard-earned knowledge to the rest of the world. And you never know, it may even make someone stop and think before he, or she, jumped headlong into their sail-boat never to be seen again.

There you have it, a year later and you are now reaping the rewards of my vast catalogue of nautical disasters. I say catalogue, there's a number of historical mishaps mentioned. However, in the main, this novel tells the story of the disaster that was a sailing trip around the North Kent Coast one dark October night.

In conclusion, the hope is, that once read and inwardly digested. If, and when the reader finds they have some kind of nautical dilemma on their hands. All they have to do is think back to these pages and then do the exact opposite. With luck, you should be as safe as houses. Not my house obviously, I had the underpinning done last year and as I did most of the work myself, it tends to lean a bit, it's next to nothing. Well, it is now... So, when I use the phrase: 'as safe as houses,' I mean a normal person's house, not mine.

This novel, is a little like presenters say on those TV crime programs: "please don't worry or lose any sleep over this, because these events are very rare."

The events depicted in this book are indeed very rare, that's true enough... True enough as long as you don't actually set foot on board a boat. If you do however, then the events which have befallen my good-self are all too liable to happen to you.

Consequently, if you feel a raging urge to sail the ocean blue, you should worry about it. You should lose sleep over it, because these things *will* happen to you. What's more, if you are in the wrong place at the wrong time, you are going to get hurt. And, if by chance, it's just not your day...

You are going to die!

It's quite a nice little book really.
I hope you enjoy it.

Chapter One

The Boat of Your Dreams
(In your dreams)

There I was forty years old, house paid for, wife, couple of kids, two cars and a rabbit. Life consisted mainly of going to work, TV dinners, a few pints of beer at the weekend and a lot of weird questions about the meaning of it all: 'Is there any point to it?' 'Where is the end of the universe?' and 'Who the hell invented nasal clippers anyway?'

It was hardly life on the edge. Then again, having said that, throwing myself of the nearest cliff was beginning to appear an attractive alternative to this safe, yet very mundane existence I had carved out for myself. Maybe I was going through the male menopause thing, then again, maybe I was just getting old.

Whatever it was, that extra spark which made the difference between simply existing and living your life to the full had grown dim. So dim, one could only see it on the darkest of nights and only then when the landlady decided on a lock-in at the pub, which fortunately for me happened quite frequently down our local.

What I needed was a diversion from the drudgery of life and if at all possible, nothing to do with beer and pubs. It couldn't be too exciting, after all I was no spring chicken, but then again, I wasn't quite ready for the comfy (though ever so slightly whiffy) cardy and slippers just yet.

A nice safe hobby, that's what we were looking for. Something that wouldn't break the bank. Something to get me out of the house and away from the Dragon and the two Monsters. Didn't have a pet name for the rabbit strangely enough. Nevertheless, I quite liked the furry member of the family, probably because it didn't moan about money or ask questions about simultaneous equations.

Fishing, a possibility I suppose, unfortunately the appeal of fishing never quite hooked me (even for me, that's a pretty awful pun... It's so bad I'm leaving it in). I would go further and say, rather than actually go fishing, I would have gladly chewed off one of my own feet. So, that would be a 'no' for fishing then.

Hang-gliding, fine, got me near cliffs for a start. There were a few drawbacks with this hobby, so I understood. It was all very exciting for the first week or two, but then after that you tended to die, something to do with the law of averages and gravity, or is that the other way around?

Snorkelling, one word: 'Sharks!' mind you, I don't believe there were too many great whites swimming around Dover harbour; you can't be too careful you know. Snorkelling? Wasn't sure. Sounded a bit too much like hard work to me. All that compressed air and heavy breathing, not to mention the rubber. Talking of which, I could always have a dalliance with one of the ladies from electronic testing, at least I wouldn't get wet. Of course, that little hobby would come with its own set of dangers. Swimming with sharks, may have been preferable to facing the wrath of a wronged wife. Especially a wife with her own set of castrating tongs. They're quite a conversation stopper at dinner parties, I can tell you.

What about sailing? Okay I'll go for that. Initial cash outlay, some mooring fees maybe, that's about it financially. Little cabin, couple of bunks for when the family get too much, probably use them quite a bit. Standing before the main brace (whatever that is), sea spray in your face; sextant in one hand; mug of rum in the other, shouting "Ahoy me hearties" and other such nautical gubbinge to all and sundry... Yes, why not? Sailing...

As it happened, I had spent some time in the Merchant Navy. For a couple of years, I was a real live Officer and a Gentleman, okay! I was just an Officer - a Third Mate. Still, my five years of service before the mast would surely stand me in good stead for bobbing around on the ocean waves on a little yacht, or so you would have thought. It had to be said, that some of my past experiences of being on the water in a professional capacity (and otherwise, if I was honest) had not always gone according to plan. As for the zealots of the nautical jargon, as far as I was concerned, if you called the galley the kitchen, or a bulkhead the wall, a big black hole was not going to open up and suck you into the depths of hell. The continual struggle to keep your cabin spick and span and generally doused with enough disinfectant, so as to be able to perform open heart surgery on the bathroom floor, should the need arise, all got a bit wearing after a while as well. Still, good old Blue Star had given me the opportunity to study navigation and even yachting theory. Consequently, as long as I didn't do anything silly, as if I would... Floating around on the briny in a bit of plastic with a big rag on top was going to be a bit of a doddle... I mean... What could go wrong?

It was all sorted. All I needed now was a boat and strangely enough it didn't take long before I found the boat of my dreams. As fate would have it, a couple of days after my momentous decision to acquire a yacht, I was standing outside the boatyard in the little town Sandwich, down in Kent. Browsing through the photographs of various craft. There right in front of my eyes, was this lovely twenty-two foot, four-berth immaculate yacht and next to this, was the one I could afford.

A little eighteen-foot six-inch yacht. A type of yacht called a Frolic 18, possibly not the most macho model name ever thought up. The boat itself went by the name of 'Solo,' can't say I was too keen on the name either, but then, what's in a name? The picture of Solo made her look a little scruffy and more than a bit tired. However, at £3,500, she was well within my price range and that was the most important factor at that particular moment in time. To hell with whether it floated or not, as long as it had the right price tag, nothing else mattered.

Money aside, this little craft seemed to have all the basics: a cabin, a couple of sails and an engine, which I considered essential. Almost as essential as somewhere to store the beers. Consequently, without further ado, I went straight round to the nearest pub to have a think about it...

Two or three pints later, the sad little yacht I was contemplating purchasing, had become the best thing since the QE2 and very nearly as big. Unfortunately, (or possibly fortunately) by the time the beer goggles had kicked in, the boatyard was closed for the night. Undeterred,

I took the details and the very next day I contacted the people selling the yacht and made arrangements to view the boat in question for the following Saturday. Of course, there was a lot of grovelling to be done to the wife, not to mention a healthy smattering of bull thrown in for good measure. Well, if you don't make use of skills you've picked up over the years, especially working in the merchant marine what's the point?

"Yes dear, just going to have a look at it, that's all..."

"And it comes with a lovely little dinghy, the kids would just love that..."

"Well, if the picture is anything to go by, I certainly won't be paying £800 for it...'

I don't think she was entirely convinced, but at least she didn't throw anything at me this time.

Saturday came around and I took the whole family to see this wonderful little craft, which I'd been praising to the high heavens for the past week or so. The yacht was berthed at a place called Oare Creek, some 30 miles up the road from where I lived. Like the riverside at Sandwich, Oare Creek's marina was also a smallish place, with only something in the region of fifty to sixty boats moored on each side of the riverbank.

We'd arrived a little early, so the man from Sandwich, who was to show us around the yacht, had not turned up as yet. However, the manager at Oare Creek pointed us in the general direction of the object we were seeking. It didn't take long before we found something vaguely resembling the picture I had seen in the boatyard window. The fact that she was the only boat on the river with a dirty great 'For Sale' sign stuck on the window, I have to admit, did help a little.

As for its name? You would have thought that would have been the easiest way of identifying a vessel. Not in this case, you had to lean over the back end to find the word 'Solo' and as the stern was facing away from the quay, it just wasn't visible. For some unknown reason, there were no markings on the bows at all. This made no difference to anything whatsoever, but I found it mildly disconcerting. What! No markings on the bows! Could this be the end of the world?

First impressions: it looked a lot better in real life than the brown, patch work, painted object depicted in the photographs. In fact, I was quite impressed. I did not know what I was expecting exactly, but my words to the wife sort of summed it up: "My God! It's a real yacht."

The wife just frowned from the jetty.

Indeed, it was a real yacht: two sails, a main and jib, a furling reef jib no less. All the rigging seemed to be in place. Two sets of shrouds each side of the mast, fore and aft stays, the forestay supporting the Jib, stainless-steel shrouds, stainless-steel fastenings and everything seemed in fairly good condition. Inside, we could see through the windows (the cracked windows it had to be said) the cabin had a galley, that is a sink and two gas burners. There was a table and a couple of bunks each side. It even had a toilet or 'head' as we professional sailors called it, tucked away in one of the corners. The kids sat in the open cockpit, looking quietly bemused, the wife still on the jetty, still frowning.

"What do you think you two?" I said to the kids.

"Uh hu..." and "it's OK..." Not what one might call a terribly enthusiastic response, but coming from our two, these comments were really quite favourable.

It wasn't long before Fred from Sandwich showed up "Hello, you found it then," he said with a big smile "Yep, the 'For Sale' sign was a bit of a giveaway" I said smiling back. He jumped aboard and pretty soon we were inside. It was all a bit tatty with the plastic interior fabric stuff coming away from the walls, sorry bulkheads. The stove could have done with a good clean, in fact a thorough spring clean throughout would not have gone amiss. Overall, it appeared to me, all we were talking about was a tub of glue to stick the covering back in place and a bucket of water and some detergent cleaner for a good old wash down.

Fred talked me through the extras, which took all of two minutes: a couple of anchors, a gas cylinder and a mouldy water container. No, no, it did have a couple of hand-held flares, two years out of date and two fire extinguishers, also two years out of date. We went out on deck; in other words, we moved two feet astern into the cockpit area. Fred explained some of the rigging and unfurled the jib. Almost everything was, or could be controlled from the cockpit, which obviously made life much easier, so I was informed.

Fred was in his fifties, a pleasant and very chatty kind of guy, he had obviously been around boats for most of his life and knew what he was talking about. However, he was there to sell me this thing and certainly from Fred's point of view, there was very little wrong with this yacht called 'Solo.' From my stand point. Well... I had to agree.

"Osmosis!" the big 'O' word of fibreglass boats. I knew vaguely what it was and what to look for. Not surprisingly, Fred assured me there was no sign of osmosis on the yacht, "that he could see," he added. By this time, we were on the jetty examining the hull. Bubbles on the gel coat. This was the tell-tale signs of osmosis and it was true to say, that there were no signs of any bubbling. Then again, the underside was fairly well caked in slime and though you could see a lot of the hull, there were certain parts of it which were well and truly hidden from view. The fact of the matter was, that the hull and the outside in general, just like the inside, could have done with a bloody good clean.

Fred and I spent another five minutes or so discussing various sailing procedures "Open reaches, closed reaches, luffing and wind over tide." When I say discussing, Fred talked and I went "yes" or "hu hu," where it seemed appropriate to do so.

The last thing he mentioned was the dingy, it was hiding up on the bank. I thought to myself: 'I could definitely have some fun with that thing...'

We left it, that I would have a think about whether I was going to go ahead and buy the yacht or not and possibly make arrangements to have another look, sometime in the following week.

On the way home, a cloak of silence had descended on the car, not so much of a worry with the kids, as they were immersed in their MP3 players. However, with the wife this could only mean one thing - the wheels were turning and I didn't mean the car wheels either. She would be busily thinking up her arguments for when I broached the subject of buying the boat: 'We can't afford it; we don't know anything about sailing and we'll all drown...' I could counter the first two, but I suppose drowning would be a bit of a problem. I stiffened my resolve and taking the bull by the horns said: "Well dear what did you think of that?"

"...What about paying for it? I thought we're going to have a new bathroom this year... And anyway, you don't know anything about sailing. You'd take us all out and get us all drowned...! Then there's the holiday to pay for..." So predictable...

"Yes, I suppose so, but..." Before I had a chance to say any more the wife was off again: "there's all the time and effort getting to and from the thing... You'll always be fiddling with it; you'd never do any work around the house any more... It would just be an excuse to go down the pub and spend more money and what about insurance... You're going to have to get insurance, you're bound to smash it up sooner or later, or worse bump into someone else's boat, that's worth hundreds of thousands... What are the children going to get out of it? It's not as if it's going to help their education, not even going to be good exercise for them and all the time..."

I don't know what it was, may have been the inflection in her voice; maybe the flaring nostrils; may have been the throbbing blue veins in her neck, but I had a sneaking suspicion, she wasn't entirely won over by the idea of me buying a little boat for the family...

After five or ten minutes, I'd switched off, realising that sailing the yacht would be child's play compared to cajoling the wife into spending money to buy me a new toy. Nevertheless, given a couple of weeks and with a lot of sweet talk, the occasional bunch of flowers, lightly sprinkled with a measured amount of grovelling, I was quietly confident that I would win her around.

A week went by and I returned to Oare Creek (without the doom and gloom merchant) to meet with the owner, which was more or less a waste of time as the tide was out and we couldn't even start the engine, let alone go for a sail. The owner was an oldish, little man, I wasn't entirely taken by him, bit shifty around the eyes. I could see him sitting behind a desk somewhere counting other people's money. Did I want to give him my money to count? That was the question. I suppose he was pleasant enough though.

My first impressions of the boat a week earlier, had been favourable and nothing I'd seen on the second visit had changed that opinion. The price was right, to coin a phrase. Admittedly, there was a bit of work to do on the wife front, but, that aside, I virtually agreed to buy the yacht there and then, two hundred quid knocked off for cash; as far as I was concerned it was well worth the money.

From the initial decision of wishing to get involved in yachting to actually owning a yacht had taken only three weeks. Of course, it might have helped if I'd actually been afloat, at least once during this period. Oh! no not me - Do first, think later... That seemed to be the attitude to most of my decision-making processes.

Sometimes you just have to jump into the deep end and you either learn to swim or you sink. All fine and dandy when you have a big, hairy, lifeguard standing next to the deep end. If the deep end happens to be the English Channel, that's a different kettle of fish and if you get it wrong, for one reason or another, it could turn into a very smelly kettle of fish.

Chapter Two

A Little History
(The Dark Ages)

No turning back now, I had gone and done it. As the owner of a yacht, I was now a member of the nautical fraternity once more, which in some ways was a good thing. On the other hand, there was a down side. I believe I may have mentioned previously that almost every boat I had set foot aboard, whether a ten-foot rowing boat or a 45,000-ton merchant ship, had ended in a disaster of one sort or another. 'Almost every boat' was a wee tad of an exaggeration, but you get the general drift. More to the point, on several occasions there had been the distinct possibility of loss of life, which I wouldn't mind, except that it was usually my life in question...

The very first of these disasters started, so I have been told, when I was the ripe old age of one whole year. Not even out of nappies and shit was happening, if you will excuse the pun...

The family, Mum, Dad, four-year-old sister and one-year old me, were all having a pleasant day out doing family type things. Part of which was a little jaunt on the River Ayr. Father paid the tuppence ha'penny to the boatman - it might not have been quite as long ago as that. Then we all jumped aboard; well, I didn't, being a mere baby and only about three inches long. Either way, we all ended up safely seated in this nice wooden rowing boat and with a gentle push (or maybe a rough push - I wouldn't know) off we went down the river.

It was a lovely day, by all accounts, blue skies, gently flowing water and not a breath of wind. The parents had brought some food along and a flask of tea to make a bit of a picnic of the whole thing. The perfect family day out, nothing could have been nicer.

So, there we all were floating around in mid-stream, my sister leaning over the side trying to see her reflection and possibly not crying for a change. Father doing his rowing bit and mother holding on to her one-year-old son (that would be me) like a good mother should. Then there was the picnic: cakes, triangular shaped sandwiches, I haven't got a clue really, but there was a flask of tea, I did know that. I'm not quite sure why we always had a flask of tea everywhere we went, but we did. I think it was just one of those things everyone did in those bygone days of yore, bit like bottles of water today. What is that all about? Is there going to be a sudden and instantaneous drought, which everyone knows about apart from me. And due to this, we must all have a bottle of water with us at all times and keep drinking from this almost constantly, just in case the drought catches us unawares.

Anyway, the flask was placed on the thwarts, the seats for you normal people, obviously on a little rowing boat, with two adults, one child and a baby; the whole thing was inherently unstable, an accident waiting to happen. Actually, it's my belief that all boats, big or small, old or new, ship-shape or not, were all in fact, accidents waiting to happen. It was just a question of time. And the time for my first nautical accident had arrived.

For whatever reason, no doubt my sister would have had a hand in it, we never did get on, the rowing boat rocked from one side to the other and of course, the first thing to go flying was the flask of tea. Instead, of letting this flask fall and smash into a hundred bits on the floor of the boat, like a proper mother. What does my mother do? In her wisdom, she decides to save the flask of tea, which is fine. After all, a nice cup of tea is just what you want on a scorching hot summer's day... But not to the exclusion of throwing your baby overboard... It seems that in her zest to collect the flask and its precious contents - the tea... My mother totally forgot about her baby... Me...

Before anyone had realised, I had gone over the side, not completely, it was true, but my head was well and truly immersed under the water. If it wasn't for my mother finally coming to her senses and forgetting about the bloody flask (a bit belatedly if you ask me) and managing to grab the disappearing baby by the ankle, I may well have slipped to a rather premature and very watery grave. Apparently, I didn't cry, but I did have a slightly startled expression on my face. I have no doubt that had I been able to verbalise my thoughts, I would have been saying: 'Oops! Worse things happen at sea.' As a one-year-old child (a very precocious child), I suppose 'oops!' would be an acceptable outburst. However, still saying 'oops!' at the age of forty, not so sure about that.

I'm digressing a little. What matters, is that the flask of tea was saved and I understand, a little later in the afternoon, everyone (apart from me) had a very nice cup of tea... So that was all right then...

My next encounter with the ocean blue was some ten years later, which had the advantage that I could actually remember it all. Although, having said that it's not one of my fondest memories...

A friend and I had decided to bunk off school and take the train thirty miles up the West Coast of Scotland to the seaside town of Largs... It was all planned down to the last detail. I went to my mate Roger's house before school, ostensibly to collect some homework. Why no one figured out that it would have been a lot more practical, for all concerned, if we had just waited till school to get this homework, I'll never know. Nevertheless, this was the ploy and it worked. The only difficult bit about our ingenious plan was catching the bus to the train station. The problem being, that the bus stop was right outside the school playground. The solution was easily solved by the pair of young criminal masterminds at work here. All we did was wait on the school side of the road, opposite the bus stop. When we observed the bus coming, we dashed across the road and proceeded to wave it down. It all went like clockwork. The only thing we hadn't factored into our devious, yet brilliant, master plan was: what the hell were we going to do at Largs for the whole day?...

I suppose we got to our seaside destination about ten thirty. By eleven o'clock we were bored. We bought ourselves a couple of ice creams and wandered down to the sea front. Here we came across the sea wall and somewhat dejectedly plonked down on it. This fantastic day of adventure we were supposed to be having, was turning into a bit of a damp squib. Sat there as we were, contemplating the cruel finger of fate and wondering if life really was a bitch, or more probably, should I have had an ice cream oyster rather than a cone... Low and behold, we hadn't realised it at first, but all our prayers were answered. Almost right in front of us was an old man renting out... Yes! You guessed it... Rowing boats...

There just wasn't any contest: two young lads out for a bit of adventure and there it was staring them right in the face. It had a bit of a sad face, as I seem to remember. Sat on his bench, as he was, this rowing-boat man, brown mac type thing, grey hair and smoking a pipe.

We approached him, more than a little nervously, to hire one of his rowing boats. As it turned out, he was quite a cheerful kind of a guy. Made some joke about not being at school, which of course was the very thing we were nervous about. Still, we got our boat for the half hour or however long it was going to be. And we didn't even have to get our money out, as it was pay on return...

The next thing, after we had managed to gain some sort of co-ordination in the rowing of the boat, was... Where could we to go?

Unfortunately, it was all too obvious. In fact, the whole morning had been a bit like that. It was as if there had been some kind of divine intervention taking place. The mysterious hand of fate (cruel or otherwise) was unerringly guiding us to exactly that... Our fate.

What was obvious?... A dirty great island, not half a mile away, or so we thought. In fact, it was probably well over a mile, but... It was a nice enough day and let's face it, it wasn't as if we had anything else to do, so off we went.

The dirty great island, commonly known as Millport (after the main town) was really not that great, even though the island was actually called the 'Great Cumbrae Island.' Still, it was big enough for us. It was a mile, maybe two miles long, so yes, even two eleven-year-olds, especially with their newly acquired rowing skills, stood a good chance of hitting it.

Oh! and by the way, this 'dirty great island,' I'm pretty sure was quite a clean island really... Wouldn't want to upset the Great Cumbrae Islanders...

Anyway, strange as it might seem and as far as memory serves, we ploughed a fairly straight course and landed on the island without any mishaps, or even the hint of a mishap. Could this be me on a boat and everything going according to plan? I don't think so...

We had a nice picnic; well, we had a picnic... Maybe it wasn't boats at all; maybe it was 'picnics' that caused all the evilness in the world? Of course! I don't know why I had not thought of this before... Okay, I'm being silly now. As if two eleven-year-old boys rowing a boat a mile out to sea wasn't silly...

We'd done it, rowed over to the island, had our picnic - the evil picnic - and that was it. There wasn't much else to do. That is, apart from the small detail of rowing that mile back to the main land... And it was getting ever so slightly windy...

We got our stuff together, what there was of it and clambered on board the extremely small, very little, wooden vessel. Then proceeded to push ourselves into the extremely large, very open, watery stuff - the Firth of Clyde - You might just be getting the picture now. Little boys; a little boat; a little tired... And lots and lots of greyish, moody looking water...

At first, I think we were doing all right, but then, that ever so slight wind became ever so slightly stronger, we rowed on... As we were stuck in a rowing boat, in the middle of the bloody ocean (well, that's what it felt like) we didn't really have much of a choice. On the way to the island, everything had been nice and smooth, with the only sound, the rhythmic splashing of the oars hitting the water. Now, on the return leg, the boat's motion was rough and juddery and as for the only sounds being the oars hitting the water... You couldn't even hear them... Splats and splashes could be heard all round the boat, but there was no comforting rhythm to any of these noises. The wind strength, in all probability, would not have been that strong, maybe a force three. The problem was that we were in an awfully small boat and any kind of wind was going to make the going extremely tough. A force three, given the size of our boat, was very much like being in a howling gale.

By about half way and with the wind still picking up, we were beginning to get ambushed with spray from time to time. I suspect around about then, a small degree of panic was beginning to take hold of the two young lads in their tiny, little boat. The only saving grace, apart from our innocence (otherwise known as stupidity) was that, the wind was on the port quarter and therefore actually blowing us towards the land. It wasn't exactly a straight course to the nearest landfall, but at least we were going in the right direction, more or less. I also seem to remember about half way there was a slight disagreement between the two of us. Roger wanted to try to get us back on course. Back to the sad faced man who'd hired us the bucking bronco we found ourselves in. As far as I was concerned, I just wanted to hit land; anywhere would have done. Just as long as I wasn't out there being tossed around in what was no more than a toy boat. However, the argument petered out as quickly as it had begun, mainly as there wasn't anything to argue over. The overriding factor was the wind. It didn't matter a jot which way we wanted to go. The plain fact of the matter was that the elements, and the elements alone, were going to decide where we would end up.

At that stage and with the wind still building, there was the very real possibility that the only place we were going to end up would be in the water. If that had happened with the waves and how tired we were, not to mention the cold, we would not have lasted more than a couple of minutes...

We struggled on, not only not arguing, but not actually talking at all for long periods. I think somewhere along the way, we had realised, despite our innocence, that we were in deep water and in more ways than one. Maybe it was this realisation that we were in serious trouble that caused us to come to a tacit understanding. Rather than fight each other, it would be a good idea to give each other a bit of encouragement:

"Keep rowing... Keep rowing!!!"

"I am rowing... You keep rowing!!!"

"Row!... Row!..."

"Keep rowing... For God's sake keep rowing!!!"

I think in the end, we both ended up in unison...

"Row!... Row!... Row!... Row!... Row!..."

One way or another there was a lot of rowing going on...

The last hundred metres were the worst. The land was so close, yet it didn't seem to be getting any closer. It was moving okay. The trouble was... It was moving sideways...

That ever so slight breeze we had first felt on the rocky shore of Great Cumbrae had now become a serious blow, with even stronger gusts. Along with the change in wind strength, had come a change in direction... We were no longer being driven towards the beach. Now, we were just being pushed down the coast parallel to the shore. The only way we were going to make the safety of land was through our own efforts... But we were getting tired, extremely tired by then...

The two if us had been at the oars for possibly thirty minutes and for two eleven-year-olds, it was hard work. It wasn't helped by the frequent occurrences of the oars failing to hit the water and then one or other of us would end up on our backs, in the bottom of the boat. This might have been funny under normal circumstance, but when it happened aboard that battered bit of wooden flotsam, no one laughed...

When we caught a crab, it would take an age to get back our rhythm. It was all time and effort wasted. The waves were beginning to break over the bulwark and spray was hitting our faces on a regular basis. We were getting very wet. Our clothes were getting heavy. There was more than an inch or two of water in the bottom of the boat, our shoes were soaked through. All these things were just adding to our problems...

Fifty metres... We seemed to be making progress at long last...

"Nearly there... Keep Rowing..."

Twenty-five metres... Twenty-four metres... Twenty-three metres...

It was slow, but finally, the bottom of the boat hit the rock-strewn seashore. If we were tired, no one would ever have believed it. You never saw two young boys move so fast in all your life... No sooner did the keel ground ashore, we were off... Jumped straight into the water and up the beach. I couldn't tell you what that was about. All I know was that we were half way up the pebbles of the shoreline, before you could say 'Shiver me Timbers.'

Eventually, we stopped running and turned around to look at the thing which had been trying to kill us for the past forty-five minutes or more.

The rowing boat, or as it was later to be known 'the boat of death' had ended up about half a mile down from the place where we had originally acquired the thing. This did have its plus side in that we didn't see the boat-man again and as a consequence were unable to pay the guy. We did think about going to find him, but that thought didn't really stay with us for too long. In fact, we really should have gone back to pull the boat up the beach a bit more. However, there was no way either of us would be going anywhere near 'the boat of death' or any other boat for that matter... Ever again...

The final bit to this story was when I was at Roger's house the following weekend. We were in his living room and his mother who was doing something with the daughter's dress, said: "I'd still like to know where you got those blisters on your hands?"

Quick as a Flash, Roger retorts: "And where do you think I got them... Rowing to Millport...?"

Brilliant... Last I heard, he was in the RAF flying helicopters... He got out of the water and I ended up back in it. Roger was a clever guy...

So, I suppose that was my first real experience of boating and although it didn't end with anything too dreadful taking place, it wasn't the most positive of experience either. If only I had heeded the warning at that youthful age, it might have saved me a lot of trouble in later life. Then again having said that and knowing me. In all probability, it would not have made the slightest bit of difference in the world.

Alakefic I call the next incident. I'm now thirteen and there are loads of adults around, so I can't be blamed for this, apart from actually being there of course. It's a bit of a weird one...

My uncle Henry had a friend called Mr Tom Crowe and he owned a very nice trimaran, the names of which was Alakefic (means something in Arabic). For whatever reason, Mr Crowe decided to sell this very nice trimaran and a couple of months later bought another boat. The new one was an old, clinker-built, fishing vessel, can't remember the name. The exciting thing for me, was that I was invited along on its maiden voyage, maiden to Mr Crowe at least and the rest of us for that matter.

We had to take the vessel form Troon to Ayr... Sorry I can't resist this:

"When the fishes swam from Troon to Ayr.

The Moon was r'oon an fair...'

When the fishes swam from Ayr to Troon.

The Moon was fair an r'oon..." Some Scottish poet type person wrote it, it's quite famous, stupid, but famous.

Anyway, back to sailing from Troon to Ayr... It was daytime by the way (no moon) and we didn't see any fish either come to that.

All was going okay, apart from me throwing up my breakfast (haggis and chips, just joking: you don't have chips with haggis). In my defence, it was more than a little choppy that day and it was a fishing vessel with a very old, very smelly, diesel engine. It didn't help, that I was the gopher, which generally involved getting the refreshments from below. This wasn't that much of a problem at first. However, to get the cans of beer and pickled egg sandwiches etc., required me to go into the bowels of this lurching, swaying, oil soaked, stench filled, fishing vessel... Wow! This is bringing back memories... I could do without this particular memory, thank you very much.

It wouldn't be the last time I would throw up because of diesel engines. That First Mate never did forgive me for ruining his shoes (that's a story for another day). Nevertheless, after a while, I did regain my sea legs and as long as I wasn't sent below too often, I was fine and even began to enjoy the trip.

Eventually we arrived in Ayr Harbour, it wasn't the greatest of ports, but big enough for the occasional coaster and the paddle steamer the Waverley of course. I say 'of course,' because my mother seemed to live on-board this thing. Every time it sailed from Ayr, my mother would be there; ok not every time, but she did go on it a lot and on the odd occasion I was dragged along, which I didn't mind as you could get a cup of tea on board... This meant that the dreaded flask was left behind...

The approach to the harbour was wide enough. The tricky bit was, that no sooner were you through the pier heads, then you had to go hard a port to get into the marina. This fairly violent manoeuvre was accomplished without any major problems, bearing in mind that this was the first time out in this unnamed fishing vessel for Mr Crowe and crew. We came around ok, but there was a lot of banging and thudding noises coming from somewhere, it didn't sound quite right at all. I was in the cockpit trying to keep out of the way. My uncle and Mr Crowe were big beefy blokes and a little nudge from either and I would have been over the side quicker than you could say: 'Oops! This water's cold.'

After the turn, I seem to remember there was a little confusion as to where exactly the vessel was to be berthed. This confusion was resolved quite quickly and it was decided that the berth was somewhere down towards the bottom of the marina, the eastern end. Consequently, off we steamed in that general direction, no problem, chugging along at about five knots I would guess, everything under control.

When we approached the berth, it seemed to me (admittedly, not that I knew a great deal about it) the obvious thing would have been to just steer straight in towards the pontoon headfirst. However, for some reason and I am sure it was valid reason, Mr

Crowe wanted to go stern first. This entailed turning around, not a problem, our skipper had done this many times before in his previous boat and that, being a trimaran, would have been a lot more awkward.

Talking of his previous boat. It just so happened, that to get to our new berth we had to sail past Alakefic. She was moored nearer the entrance and on the opposite wall to our new berth... Did I say this was a bit of a weird one?

We commenced the turn to port, it was a tight space to manoeuvre a twenty-eight foot, rather sluggish, clinker built, fishing vessel. It didn't help matters that everything was an unknown quantity for the motley crew on board. Suffice it to say, there was a fair bit of cursing and swearing going on. The main problem seemed to be something to do with getting the thing into gear. It was fine when she was in gear, it was just that there was a lot huffing and puffing (and swearing) to force that cast-iron lever (it was a good twelve inches long) into forward or astern.

We were about three quarters the way through the turn to port. Mr Crowe slowed the revs and attacked the gear leaver once more, again there was a lot crunching, followed by some swearing, but finally, he did manage to engage forward. Once in gear, he started swinging the wheel to turn the head more to port, there was a few seconds of calm. The engine was just on idle by this time. Nevertheless, we were still picking up speed... Then came the time to take her out of gear... Oh! Dear...

There wasn't any crunching of cogs or grinding of gears this time. In fact, there wasn't any noise from the gear box at all. The reason, it was well and truly jammed in forward... That's not to say there wasn't any noise... The swearing had started up again and it had started up again with a vengeance...

The gears were locked solid and we were trundling ahead at a fair old rate of knots, especially for the confined area of the harbour. Fortunately, we didn't appear to be in any danger of hitting anything, well, not at that particular juncture in time. We were steaming towards the western wall, the entrance really and it was a good fifty to sixty yards away, so we were in no immediate danger of doing any damage to our boat or anything else. The swearing died to a low murmur...

All that was necessary, was to switch the engine off, steer for some clear water and allow the vessel to glide to a soft landing when the speed had come off... Absolutely, nothing to worry about what so ever... What could possibly go wrong? ... Well, I was on board for one thing...

Mr Crowe went to turn the ignition key, which he did... Did the engine gurgle and splutter to a stop? ... No! ... Did the swearing increase in intensity... Oh! Yes...

Mr Crowe and my uncle were becoming a little fraught, still it wasn't the end of the world: the engine was just on tick over and we were heading for the harbour wall. There might be a little damage, but if everyone fended off, the impact might not be that bad.

Things were about to take yet another turn for the worse, literally as it happened. For no reason, our smelly, old fishing vessel; our evil, smelly old fishing vessel decided to alter course.

"Turn the bloody steering wheel will you!" My uncle was definitely becoming a little fraught, his big, bright red face, getting redder by the second.

"I am turning the 'bleeping bleep'... It's 'bleeping' stuck..." Mr Crowe's face, by now, had a distinct tinge of red about it as well. So, along with everything else, our steering was now jammed... The tempo and volume of the swearing increased very dramatically... And when our little, but very out of control vessel turned onto her new heading, a heading that would put us on a collision course with (three guesses) Alakefic... All I can say is that, it was just as well I'd been schooled at a comprehensive. Otherwise, I might have been quite shocked at the torrent of expletives coming forth from my elders and betters. Both of whom were straining at the helm in a vain attempt to avoid a collision. My uncle especially: he was leaning over at an angle of forty-five degrees pulling on to the wheel for all he was worth. I was just waiting for the wheel to come away from the deck and see Mr Crowe and my uncle disappear over the side.

Now that would have been something, alas this didn't happen.

All their efforts were completely futile. The gears were locked solid and the engine refused to switch off. We were trundling forward and at ever-increasing speed. More than that, we were still heading straight for Alakefic... It was as if we were actually aiming for Tom Crowe's old boat. A little spooky if you ask me. I could understand the gears getting jammed, even the engine not switching off, but altering course of its own accord and heading for Alakefic. And on top of all that, the steering jams... No Way... Just plain weird. On the other hand, we were going to hit something, so it might as well have been Alakefic. At least she would be softer than a concrete wall.

By the time we were about ten feet away, everyone had accepted the inevitable. There was some scampering around moving fenders and stuff. Mr Crowe had the engine cover off and was head first down the hole and I was holding on for dear life.

Then came the crunch, well it was more of a grinding, scraping noise really. Whatever kind of noise, it practically sheered through one of Alakefic's floats. One good thing though... It did slow us down... And strangely, no swearing.

And that was the end of that escapade, almost... The guys (a consortium of three) whom Mr Crowe had sold his boat to, were not there on the day of the collision. However, the next day Mr Crowe went along to explain the reason why sizable chunks of their new boat were floating around Ayr harbour. I wasn't there, but I understand quite a bit of swearing took place. Now there's a surprise.

I don't suppose the Alakefic affair had a lot to do with me really, but it was kind of funny. Especially if you were a shy, retiring, thirteen-year-old boy, who hadn't heard loads of adults shouting and swearing their heads off at each other before.

I think that's enough history for now. So, I won't bore you with the time we stole, I mean borrowed my cousin's boat at three o'clock in the morning and got his pride and joy slightly wet... On the inside. We sank basically. I don't know what my cousin was moaning about, we repaired the hole... Sort of...

The week on the Norfolk Broads: four eighteen to nineteen-year-old lads on this Broads cruiser. Let's just say, when we returned the boat - when it got towed back, we didn't feel it was appropriate to ask for our £100 deposit back...

I won't mention the time I got hit in the face with a rope going through the Panama Canal. Mind you, spending ten days in a Panamanian hospital wasn't a bundle of laughs, not to mention the week in a Canterbury hospital, or the week in specialist eye hospital in London...

The time we rammed our sister ship in the Straits of Hormuz. Captain 'Smith' definitely required a stiff drink to steady his nerves that day, not that he needed an excuse to partake of a little alcoholic refreshment, but only after the sun had gone over the yard arm. He was very good like that...

I won't mention the time I went for a swim in Dunkirk harbour after trying to climb up the mooring ropes, there might have been a little drink (or two) involved in this episode as well. It would have been all right if there had only been a single mooring rope, but as there were two side by side, about a tenth of the way up, if that, the ropes decided to part. I was left spread-eagled between them and there was only one way to go... Splash... My head just missed the side of the concrete quay by inches... Might have knocked some sense into me. Then again, it would almost certainly have killed me…

I won't mention the time I had to walk the gangplank – the gangway. Twelve o'clock at night, the wind had spring up and all but one of the stern lines had parted, the back end of the ship was fifty metres off the quay… And guess who had to go find the shore-side mooring team… Ten-thousand-ton ship and there was only three of us on-board (ship was at re-fit). Got to the gangway on the foredeck, by this stage, the front of the ship was also off the dock wall and by a good twenty feet. The gangway was reaching the end of its travel… "Get across there, you'll be alright," the mate shouts on the radio… "If I die here, I'm going to come back and haunt you…" was my reply... I shot across that aluminium frame at ninety miles an hour... Just as well, ten seconds later not even that, five second and the gangway was in the water. Did I get 'a well done for risking my life'? Did I get 'a thank you'? Did I get anything? ... Nadda... Not a sausage... Me? Bitter? ... No! ...

As for the shark in the ship's swimming pool. I believe we were off Cape Town, or was it Sydney. Somewhere down there. Anyway... Thinking about it, makes my eyes water even now.

And then there was the time we popped into Mobil, Alabama for a beer. Nice establishment, 'Lafayette' I remember the places was called, the name should have given us a clue really... Wall to wall men! I use the term 'men' in its loosest possible meaning here. No... You definitely don't want to know about that...

Chapter Three

Teach Yourself Yachting
(In three easy lessons)

And so, the day came when I was on-board Solo and very nearly afloat. This is when a touch, just a touch mind you, of reality struck home. I was tugging at this, heaving at that and generally fiddling around and each time I did so, I said to myself: "Do you know what you're doing?" and each time the answer came back, "not a bloody clue!"

Even more reality would be sinking in, if my newly acquired craft didn't float. I suddenly remembered that, as yet, I had not actually seen the yacht afloat. I had visions of water spurting from every corner and there I would be, standing on the deck saluting as the vessel slowly submerged beneath the waves, or in this case the murky waters of the river Oare.

The deed was done - bought and paid for. It was all a little too late to start worrying as to whether the thing was going to float or not. I continued to fiddle around regardless. After all there was precious little I could do had water started to flood into the cabin. That vision aside, I was pretty confident that the craft would remain intact when subjected to the rigors of the mighty river Oare. The mighty river Oare may have been overstating it a bit. The river, when the tide was out, was about three feet across. That was neither here nor there, if there was a hole in the hull, the size of the river would not make the slightest difference, I would still sink. She would float, I had no doubts and sure enough, pottering about as I was, suddenly I became aware that everything was moving...

"Oh my God! We're afloat!"

Fortunately, there was no one around to hear the shock and surprise in my voice. I'll never be quite sure why I was so surprised that a yacht should actually float, but there you are. The next question arose:

"What the bloody hell do I do now?... Engine! That would be a good idea..."

The engine was a little four horsepower outboard, which dropped into a well at the stern of the vessel (not that I had seen many outboards at the front end, you understand). It was already in position, one of my more constructive fiddling moments. I played with the controls on the front panel of the machine, as if I knew what I was doing. Gave the cord a couple or three pulls and blow me the thing fired into life.

Now I was in the proverbial... There was no going back, no reason to put it off any longer... I was going to sea, well pootle up and down the river for half an hour. It was my maiden voyage; I was allowed a few butterflies.

Fortunately, it was a weekday and this meant that there were fewer people around than usual. Indeed, the only person I could see was some old guy, on the other side of the Oare tarting up his boat and he was a good bit up river from me anyway. Nevertheless, I still felt a little self-conscious, as though the eyes of the world were upon me. This may have had something to do with the worry in the back of my brain: once let loose on the river, I could well end up destroying everything in sight, which might have been a tad on the embarrassing side.

Engine started, the next thing to be done of course was to: "Loose off the main brace, cut free the shackle pin, avast me hearties with the mooring cleaty jib luffing bejanglers... Otherwise known as untying the boat from the jetty. So, with great aplomb (whatever that means - no doubt it has some nautical genus or other) and trying to act as casual as possible, I jumped off the yacht and commenced undoing the knots holding the boat to the jetty.

Strangely, I did have a plan of action: basically, untie the thing, push it into the river and jump on-board... What I was going to do after that, was anyone's guess? I had another surreptitious look around to see if anyone was watching, no one was...

"Okay let's do it!" I untied the ropes and even had the presence of mind to hold on to one of them. As Solo began to move out into the river, the stern, as the tide took it, started to point up river. In other words, the pointy bit was facing the right way. This was just as it should be. The old bugger, who had sold me the yacht, had mentioned it was very straightforward to get out of the berth and so far, his predictions were coming true.

"Oh buggery!" The end of the jetty - "I'd better jump..." Next thing I knew I was on-board, the engine had been engaged (in forward gear, amazingly enough) the boat was pointing in the right direction and I was at the helm steaming down the river...

"Bloody hell! That was easy..." I whispered to myself, feeling quite elated with my yachting prowess. I didn't know what bewildered me the most, the fact that I was actually sailing down the river on my own yacht or the fact that I hadn't rammed anything - yet.

The old guy on the other side of the river stopped what he was doing and gave me a wave and a nod; I waved back, being the polite person that I am. I was soon to learn that waving, when sailing on a yacht, was compulsory. I'd go so far as to say; on a busy river, you'd probably get more waves, then if paddling along Margate beach. It was a little unnerving at first – "who is this strange weirdo waving at me? … And blow me, there's another one at it." It didn't matter whether they were on the river itself or walking their dog on the bank, or quietly having a pee into Oare Creek: if you went pottering past in a yacht you got waved at… The scary thing about this waving business was, that after a short while, I found myself doing it as well, and without being waved at first.

'Oh, there's something moving… Better wave at it!'

Man, or woman, a double-decker bus, passing wildebeest... It didn't matter, just give it a wave.

Apart from the wavy thing, which was quite nice, I suppose, in a strange sort of way, everything was pretty cool, as my son would say. My language would have been more like: 'It's far out man!' However, if I ever used any terms remotely connected to the sixties, my kids would look at me as if I had just emerged from an ancient Egyptian tomb, so everything was cool... man!

The whole experience was very exhilarating; there's this sense of achievement of overcoming the forces of Mother Nature. Admittedly, sailing down Oare Creek wasn't quite sailing round the Horn in mid-winter and may not have been a big thing for

Chey Blythe, but for me - this was a big thing.

I was standing before the mast - I was standing behind the mast really, but who cares about minor details like that, sea spray in my face, well I got splashed from my mop earlier on, wind in my hair, yes definitely had the wind in the old hair. No rum, but I had a flask of vegetable soup... almost the same...

Yes, it was true: I wasn't going around The Horn in the depths of winter, but in my little world, this was pretty damn exciting stuff... And I was heading out to sea. Whether I would have the courage (for courage read stupidity) to take the boat out to sea, unaccompanied; never having been in a yacht before and not a bloody clue what I was doing, was anyone's guess, because as sure as hell, I didn't know.

One thing I did know, and that was to keep a check on the petrol tank. Although I had moaned about the old duffer who sold me the boat, he had been right about how easy it was to leave the berth. The other piece of information he'd imparted was that I should keep an eye on the petrol, it was only a small tank and he himself had been caught out while sailing somewhere or other. The last thing I needed was to be stuck out in the middle of some busy shipping lane without an engine... All right, I wasn't going to be run down by a dirty great oil tanker in the Oare river estuary. Even so, without any means of control, I would be in serious trouble.

That worry aside, sailing along the river, in my own little boat was okay... Forget the bull, forget the boss, forget the nautical terminology crap, forget the wife and the money... This was okay... 'Oh dear! Who put that stupid bit of wood there? ... Hold on... Think that's a navigational marker... This is my kind of stuff... Bits of wood for channel markers... Yea...! Blue Star was never like this...'

Forty-five minutes had gone by, loads of waving and a bit of messing around, manoeuvring and getting stuck on the bank. It wasn't my fault entirely. If that first primitive, who decided to throw a bit of tree trunk in the water to see what happened, had decided not to bother, then I would not have been burrowing my way into the Kent country side... Oh no! Definitely not my fault.

All I had tried to do was to set the sail, the one at the front end, on a stretch of the river which was somewhat wider than the rest. So, I was really sailing and everything had worked fine. Unfortunately, under sail the yacht was not as controllable as with the engine and well... I rammed the riverbank. I saw it coming and tried valiantly to avoid it. However, I suspect, if anyone had been watching, they would have thought there must be a fire on-board, hence the reason why this lunatic was aiming for the bank.

'Silly place to put a riverbank anyway... Bloody hell! It was right next to the river...'

I had to utilize a bit of nautical common sense, because I was well and truly stuck. I shoved the engine in reverse... not astern. As the panic had crept in, so the nautical jargon had gone out the window. Then whacked the revs up and weaved the bit of wood connected to the steering thingy back and forth with some vigour and managed to claw myself out of the mud. And yes, the most important factor: no one saw a thing... So, I was still the greatest sailor since Popeye... And that was all that mattered.

After my spat with the land, I continued down river, forgetting the sails for the time being. Soon the river began to widen and the number of vessels floating around me increased, so much so that I had to remember some sailing rules to avoid crashing into this other shipping. Considering the size of the river, some of this shipping was of a reasonable size. Did not know where they were going up Oare Creek. All I knew was that I didn't want these floating lumps of metal running me down.

As these bigger craft went by, there were two of them in fairly quick succession, they made the yacht bounce around quite briskly, which was okay, it gave me a feel for Solo. However, it must have been only a couple of minutes later, Solo was bouncing around very nicely, thank you very much, but this time, there wasn't any other vessels trundling past.

The riverbank was no longer a couple of swimming strokes away, but a quarter of a mile or more.

"What the hell am I doing out here?" On realizing how far I was away from the land; I undoubtedly felt a wee bitty on the nervous side.

At least there was plenty room now, I could use the sails without bumping into the Garden of England again.

After gaining some composure, tentatively, I pulled on the rope to raise the foresail and before long I was under sail; I even had the temerity to switch off the engine... Now all I had to do was turn the thing around and head for home. I'd done my bit for the day: sailed the thing under the power of the wind, all be it, only for a few minutes and just using the foresail. That was more than enough for the first time. 'Let's get the hell out of here and into the nearest pub.'

The wind was an easterly and the crests of the waves were just beginning to break, which as far as I remembered from my merchant navy days, meant I was in a force three. Ideal sailing conditions, if you knew what you were doing. That put me out of the equation straight away.

I was on a north easterly course, more or less, the boat's compass wasn't terribly easy to read, so I was sailing about forty-five degrees off the wind and doing quite a nice lick through the water, leaving a little wake behind me and everything. 'This sailing business, it's a piece of cake...'

'Okay, how do we turn this little baby around? Wind from over there, tiller up wind and around we go, no problem,' or so I thought.

I pulled on the tiller and the boat's head began to turn to port, further off the wind. The foresail filled out, making all sorts of cracking noises, then, without warning, the yacht lurched over onto her port side, leaving me scrabbling to find some kind of handhold.

'Sod this! Let me off this crate...!' I was not amused one little bit.

I straightened the tiller up, almost instinctively and everything seemed to calm down, which was fine, except we were still gong in the wrong direction.

'Never mind eh! They tell me Essex is nice this time of year...'

All was not lost. The yacht had turned halfway round to where we wanted to be. I just had to get this floating death trap (not that my attitude had changed at all from two minutes earlier) around the rest of the way... I had let the sheet (rope thingy) out, so as the sail would fill up more, which I thought was fairly nautical of me. The trouble was, that I now had to get the sail on the other side of the bit of wire stuck at the front end holding the foresail up. It seemed to me in order to do this I would have to let go one of the sheets, pull like buggery on the other and at the same time keep the tiller over, so the yacht would turn to port.

I was going to have to do damn near three things at once and all under control. Not to mention the other factor: I had to do all this, whilst not falling out of the boat... 'No way Pedro...! I'm out of here...' I was not over confident in my ability to be able to carry out this manoeuvre, without some disaster befalling me. Then again, that's why I bought the boat, for a bit of excitement, not entirely sure I wanted quite this much though.

If I wanted to be a yachty, this was the kind of manoeuvre I would have to do and do with ease. It was slowly beginning to dawn on me that there was a bit more to this sailing lark than I may have bargained for. And it wasn't as if I could pick up the phone, dial the RAC and say: "Got a problem here mate any chance of some help?"

That was the trouble with yachts and boats in general, once you've let go that line that ties you to the shore, you are kind of on your own: can't just put the brakes on and jump out the door.

There wasn't much else for it. I had a look around, not quite sure what I was looking for, inspiration probably, or possibly something a bit more practical. An inshore lifeboat would not have gone amiss.

I gave sigh of resignation, frowned somewhat and then pulled the tiller over hard, or hard over if you like, uncoiled the rope around the left ratchet windy thingy and let it go. Solo began to turn and lean over at the same time and then she began to lean more and then more. The foresail started to flap around wildly, making whiplash sounds. I was at a very strange angle, trying as I was to hold the tiller over with my backside, while madly grasping at the sheet to pull the sail around to the other side, it was all very awkward and I should imagine not at all pretty to look at.

The boat was lolling around from side to side; bits of rope were flying everywhere. The sail flapping back and forth, sometimes filling up and thrusting the yacht over, at other times the sail would suddenly be sucked back and the vessel would roll upright again. All the while I was being rocked back and forward like some kind of demented spinning top. It was a bit hectic, to say the least.

However, despite all the chaos and confusion, not to mention a lot of swearing, the boat continued to slowly come round and with a final crack of the sail, which luckily was on the right side of the forestay, filled with wind and the boat began to sail as it should. A little more pulling of this and tugging at that and bugger me boots, I was actually pointing in the right direction. I wouldn't say I was over impressed with the whole operation, but at least I was heading back towards the river and more than that, I was still dry.

About an hour later I had sailed up the river, under power of course, straight into the finger berth, almost like I'd done it a hundred times before. Tied her up, fore and aft, unshipped the engine, stuck it down below, locked up the hatch and I was gone. The nearest pub beckoned.

So, that was my first real experience of sailing and although it had had its problems, by and large, I was quite happy with what had taken place. In fact, you could say, by the end of that evening I was very happy with the day's events, mind you by that stage I was three sheets to the wind, or for the less nautical amongst you: as drunk as a skunk.

Next weekend I was out again, this time with all the family. And how they had looked forward to it all week, I can tell you...

"Do we have to go Dad? I want to do my homework this weekend" and "I'm not going on that thing without a life jacket, safety harness and a direct link to the coast guard..." No, it has to be said that their enthusiasm was on the whole, a little short of what I had hoped. Despite all this, when we arrived at the boat, everyone clambered on-board and proceeded to scuttle into the cabin, not saying a word. They were obviously in awe of the situation...

Undeterred by their lack of support, I busied myself with readying the boat for sea; this mainly entailed attacking my daughter with her teddy bear. Monster defeated; we were soon already to go.

We had to wait awhile, as the tide had not come in quite enough to float the yacht. This all added to the excitement, or in the wife's case, the tension. It wasn't too long before Solo began to wobble about, much to the bemusement of the kids and the anxiety of the wife. Secretly, I was enjoying the whole experience: the look of expectation on the kid's faces was fair enough, but to enjoy the look of fear in my wife's eyes was possible a little on the malicious side.

The kids got their brand-new life jackets on and very expensive life jackets they were too. Unfortunately, the wife and I would have to go without on this trip, which was okay, 'cause I could swim...

"We're not going to put the sail up are you?" the wife's voice full of trepidation.

"Of course, not dear," I said somewhat unconvincingly. This wasn't a lie, because I didn't know what I would be doing myself once we were underway and in the river.

I started the engine which burst into life after the third or fourth attempt. There was quite a bit of smoke and noise coming from the machine, which didn't calm the nerves of a certain member of the crew, so much so that I thought she was going to burst into tears at any moment. I'm afraid, I didn't have any sympathy for her, as far as I was concerned there was absolutely nothing to worry about. As long as I didn't do anything stupid of course...

I let go the ropes and pushed the boat out, literally in this case and when I jumped back on-board the yacht rocked quite violently, this caused quite a commotion from the cabin. I shouted to the inside: "I don't think you lot would have been much good on the Titanic." Under the circumstances, this might not have been the most tactful of comments.

The boat faced downstream nicely and I put the engine in forward gear, turned up the revs and away we went. Pretty soon the kids emerged from the cabin and started showing a little more interest. Even the wife began to lighten up and after a while some colour began to return to her cheeks as well.

About half an hour had gone by and the kids were getting into the swing of things and wanted to steer the boat. My son even had to point me in the right direction on one occasion. I had started to go the wrong side of one on the poles showing the navigable area of the river. My excuse: I was just keeping them on their toes, in actual fact I had simply not seen one of the poles (when I say poles, I mean bits of trees, technically known as whinnies) and had just assumed that the deep channel was on the wider part of the river, in this case obviously not. Still no damage done, this time at least.

Soon the river widened and became slightly bumpy and there was a little spray around. Again, this all added to the excitement for the kids and they were beginning to enjoy themselves. The wife on the other hand just kept asking: "When are we going to turn around and go home?"

There was plenty of sea room and as long as I didn't attempt any tacking, or other such strange manoeuvres, it would be all right. The wind was behind us and more or less on a whim, I pulled on the sheets for the foresail, it started to unfurl. My wife began to shout at me:

"You said you wouldn't do that!"

"Oh yes! I forgot, sorry dear..." I said to her, trying not to smile too much.

The wind took the sail and we began to put on quite a bit of speed. Everything appeared to be running rather smoothly. I must admit, I didn't dare switch the engine off, just in case I couldn't get it started again; then we would have been in trouble.

After about ten minutes, the wife's protestations became too much and I attempted to turn the boat around under sail. Not a good idea... The bloody thing heeled over so much that even I was shocked, a few colourful expletives may have passed my lips, yet another ticking off from 'she that must be obeyed.' The wind was coming from the stern and as I tried to turn, the boat's sail was broadside on to the wind and all it wanted to do was push the boat over sideways. I resumed course, pulled the foresail down smartish, revved up the engine and around we went, without too much bother.

After that, to use another nautical phrase: it was a piece of cake (sailors eat cake don't they...) We actually did the trip back up the river a great deal faster than coming out, as the tide on the return leg was running with us. It made a big difference; probably took us about an hour to get to the point where we turned around in the estuary, but not much more than half an hour to get back to the berth. Which pleased the wife immensely.

All in all, I thought it was another pretty successful mission accomplished, the kids certainly enjoyed it, for the most part and the wife certainly enjoyed getting off the boat. And, of course, no one got killed, which I always think is a plus when you return from a long sea voyage.

We all went out in the yacht once more. On the next occasion, I had my mother along, she was staying with us for a few days. Again, we just went down river for an hour played with the sails for five minutes and then turned back, no problem what so ever and there was the added bonus of having the inside of the boat spring cleaned by the mother. I don't think she went anywhere without her bottle of Cif. Mind you, it will always be Jif to her.

So that was the boat training: approximately three, two-hour trips up and down the river.

I did have the main sail up all the way once, didn't like it very much. The boat was swaying back and forth like some kind of frenzied pendulum, just as well we were tied up alongside at the time, otherwise I would have been really scared...

I had read the instructions for the depth sounder, didn't understand them, but I had read them. Swabbed the decks and cleaned the hull. Good grief! What more experience was necessary to sail forty or fifty miles round the coast, possibly in the dark, in the depths of winter, towing a dinghy and single-handed. Good God! You could do it in half an hour... in a car.

That last trip, with the mother and family, was on the Monday, come Thursday afternoon, I fully intended to move my yacht from Oare Creek around the coast to Sandwich. As long as I checked the weather before I left and no hurricanes was headed my way, I was quite sure everything would be fine.

At least that's what I kept telling myself...

Chapter Four

The First Leg
(Oare Creek to Herne Bay)

The Thursday came around, I checked the weather for the next twenty-four hours on teletext: Windy, SW'ly force three to four, well I needed a bit of wind, didn't I?...

I looked out the window from my bedroom. It was a lovely day. Light winds, cloudy fine and clear. That is the way it would have been written up in the ships log, not that I had a ship's log, of course. I did have four cheese and onion sandwiches, a packet of cigarettes and six cans of beer.

In fairness to myself, I had acquired a chart from a friend, a second mate on one of the cross-channel ferries. More of an acquaintance, than a friend. A real friend would have come up with a complete map of the area. The chart my 'friend' had given me, only showed the latter part of my journey. What, was I just meant to guess about the first seventeen miles? ...

Also, this piece of paper was so old, I think it was printed on parchment. It must have been about forty years out of date, held together with bits of sticky tape. So old, at the time of printing, I don't think they knew how to print in colour. This did have the slight disadvantage, in that depth contours on modern charts were depicted in colour, making it nice and easy to read, especially when sailing at night and inshore. A quick glance at the chart would give you a good indication whether you were sailing into dangerous waters or not. I didn't need any of that malarkey, this would have made life far too easy. Besides, charts cost money, twenty quid or there abouts, so I was told. This, twenty quid may have been invaluable in saving one's life, but what the hell, who needs a bit of colour on their chart anyway.

That's only for wimps and sailors...

I shouldn't grumble about my mate the second mate. All he said was that he might find something for me and he did. It was as much use as a chocolate tea pot, but he found me something.

Colour or no, I had planned my route on this patch work chart with great detail. Nothing was left to chance, apart from completely ignoring the fact that I would be towing dingy... Oh! And not having a chart for the first seventeen miles of the journey was a little disconcerting too. However, this part of the trip would definitely be accomplished during the day, unless something disastrous had taken place and it wasn't like I would be ten miles off shore. So, yes, there were concerns, but I was confident there wouldn't be too many insurmountable problems. Unfortunately, what I failed to grasp was that, one insurmountable problem would be all it would take to put an end to my travel plans and perhaps an end to me as well...

High water at Oare Creek was 14.02, the boat would be afloat roughly an hour and a half before that time, so I would be departing the berth around 12.30 Thursday the 30th September 1999. Three miles downriver to The Swale estuary and the commencement of passage. We professional sailors didn't officially start the journey until we had reached the open sea and as I didn't want to take any risks, I had to get the paperwork right...

12.30 Depart berth, one hour down river, against the tide.

13.30 Commence Passage, course variable for seventeen miles.

This bit was a little vague I have to admit, mainly because I had to use my road atlas. Nothing wrong with that, it had the important jutty out bit at Whitstable where I had to change course.

16.30 Second-waypoint (first on the chart), course 085 degrees Magnetic, distance 5.5 nautical miles.

We're cooking with gas here: '085 degrees Magnetic, nautical miles,' eh! eh! eh! Talk about salty old sea dog. Just give me a bit of twine, a Tesco's shopping bag and a rusty needle and watch me sail around the world... I can sort of see the twine and needle... But Tesco's shopping bag? Probably best not to think too deeply about that one.

Back to the real world of delusion and my wonderful scribblings:

17.30 Third waypoint course: 145 degrees (M), distance 2 nm.

18.00 Fourth waypoint, course: 189 degrees (M), distance 3 nm.

18.30 Fifth waypoint, course: 260 degrees (M), distance 3 nm.

19.00 End of passage.

20.00 Up the river all tied up and in the pub for a well-deserved drink or two.

Oh! I did a fantastic job working out my waypoints and courses. My parallel rulers were gliding across the chart like greased lightening, except when they caught the sticky tape. My compasses were twiddled like they'd never been twiddled before. I had tide tables out, calculators, spent hours working out the set and rate of currents from the diamonds on the chart, adding a knot to my speed here, talking half a knot off there. Put bearings to bits and bobs on the chart for the waypoints, circled this and circled that. Oh! Bloody hell, by the time I had finished, my chart was almost a work of art, black and white work of art, but you can't have everything.

Just a shame it was all a complete waste of time...

I arrived at Oare Creek early on the Thursday morning, all my goodies in hand. I spent some time messing around as usual. My biggest problem would be getting the dinghy from the edge of the yard to the river. As it happened the dinghy was not as heavy as I thought it might have been and I managed the task in no time at all. I found some old rope which had been languishing in one of the lockers of the boat for God knows how long, tied the dinghy to the back of the yacht and that was that. In the end, I actually had time on my hands while I waited for the tide to float Solo. Consequently, I put my feet up and had a cigarette and a can of beer. It was all very relaxing and peaceful. Little did I know, but this was definitely the calm before the storm.

Sure enough the tide came in. Virtually dead on half past twelve, the yacht had started to float and my little adventure was about to begin. The engine fired up at the third attempt, I jumped out of the boat and untied the two remaining ropes from the quay and pushed the boat out. Fortunately, the dinghy was swept up the river and its rope kept well away from the propeller. All in all, another textbook departure from the berth. Boy! was I good at this. Once clear of the jetty, I shoved the engine in forward gear, turned the handle for the revs and I was on my way.

It was a nice day, the sun was shining, birds twittering, the wind a little fresh, but that is what was required. Last thing I wanted was to be stuck off the North Kent coast travelling at two knots or less, I'd have been there for days... No, for the back end of September, I don't think you could have asked for a better sailing day.

As the engine puttered away, driving me down the river, I looked over my shoulder at the yacht's berth and sort of said good-bye to it. Then I thought to myself, I would probably be back in about half an hour. Knowing me, I would take one look at the sea, say, "Sod this!" and return for the safety of the river and the old berth. Then again, spending another night at Oare Creek would have cost me money, an extra month's berthing fees in fact. In truth, I would have been more likely to say: "Never mind the bloody sea, I'm not forking out any more money..." In other words, (just like the chart business) I didn't care whether it was safe or not, just as long as it didn't cost any money. One has to say, this may not have been the most pragmatic of viewpoints to have for my little trip, especially when taking to the sea on your own, no proper chart, no communication (cost money) and more or less for the first time.

As I say... What could go wrong...?

The old guy, who I had seen on my first day on the river was still there, still wearing the same pair of jeans and tatty old jumper and if I wasn't mistaken still working on the same bit of wood. He gave me a nod and kind of wry smile as Solo sailed past, I believe a nod was like one up, from a wave in the sailing fraternities book of etiquette. I waved back of course. As I went by, I remember feeling slightly uneasy about that wry smile: "Did this real old sea dog, know something I didn't?"

For the next hour or so, while I sailed towards the estuary, I occupied myself clearing the decks of unnecessary clutter and generally getting the boat ship shape for sea. There wasn't a great deal to do as it happened, but even the little I did have to do wasn't as straight forward as it might have been. I had to keep the yacht motoring in a relatively straight line, while I dashed up front to collect one of the mooring ropes, or whatever it was that required to be done. This meant leaving the tiller and even though I had a rope tied around it to keep it in the middle, once you left the tiller, you had twenty seconds, if you were lucky, to do whatever it was before the boat went off at tangent. It caused a few hairy moments, but fortunately, nothing too dramatic, just the occasional heart attack.

Then there was the old problem of the waving, as you were just about to do something, you had to stop to give somebody a wave. I even gave it a name in the end: the persistent waving problem, or the PWP for short. 'Oh! oh! here comes another PWP, smile at the ready, raise arm, slight motion, lower arm, there we go PWP over and back to reality...'

It was all very pleasant. No bosses, no phones, no back biting. At the particular moment in time, I didn't have a care in the world. This was what life was all about, I thought to myself. And it was...

Once the channel widened out to some degree, I climbed onto the cabin roof and managed to get the mainsail up. It took a fair bit of heaving on the ropes and required two attempts. As per usual, the ship's head began to veer off course as I was on the roof pulling away merrily. I had to tie the sail off quickly and dash back to the tiller to get the boat back on course.

Eventually, the mainsail was up and shortly after the foresail was filling with the wind as well. The foresail was easy enough as the sheets for this sail lead into the cockpit. As Fred had said: it did indeed make life a lot easier, no messing around clambering over the top of the boat and it was certainly a lot safer.

The wind was from the South West and I was steering a course of North East in other words the wind was coming in back of me somewhere. This suited me just fine, as long as the wind was coming from my rear, so to speak, I was quite happy: setting the sails for wind from the stern was fairly obvious. The trouble would arise when I had to do the tacking thing and sail into the wind. I had read the books; I knew what I was doing...

The engine had been whirring away for about fifty minutes. I was well into the estuary by this stage and I had a clear run to the headland off Whitstable. There was no real reason to have the engine working any further; after all I couldn't keep it running for the next eight hours. The thing was, that it was a bit like the point of no return, a psychological thing, I suppose. It was as if, once I pressed that button, I was saying to myself: 'that's it, there was no going back now!' In truth, I could turn back at any time. Nevertheless, it was a big moment when the time came to press that little red button to switch the engine off. I took a deep breath and pressed the button. Even I did not know what the fuss was about. I could always switch the thing back on again.

Then there was silence, or very nearly. Compared to the vibration and noise when the engine was running, the sounds of the waves splashing against the hull was virtual silence. These rhythmic lapping noises were also very reassuring, as it meant my eighteen-and-a-half-foot yacht was moving forward and under the power of the sails alone. Up until that moment, the engine had only been switched off once before and that was for no more than few minutes. Now I really was sailing and with both sails, it all felt pretty satisfying.

I had been making good time, but then I had had the engine on for most of the journey thus far. On the other hand, as I didn't have a chart for this part of the trip, I didn't have any means of telling what speed I was actually doing anyway. This may well have been a little faux par on my behalf...

By 13.30 I had altered course, steering East by North, well I was just pointing the bows roughly in the direction I wanted to go, not really following any particular course. The wind was well up my stern now, both sails set on the port side, strangely enough everything was going rather well.

Soon I was well out to sea, once again I did not know exactly how far off the shore the boat was, about a mile, maybe a mile and a half. This was somewhat further away than I would have liked to have been and if the truth were known I wasn't quite sure how I had managed to get so far out. One minute I was sailing out of the Oare river estuary, with the shore line no more than a couple of hundred yards away, the next time I looked, I could hardly see the bloody beach. Got to say, I felt a little nervous once again, on realising how far I had drifted away from the land. 'Not to worry,' these were my father's favourite words; I have a sneaky feeling he would have said these words had he been falling over a cliff. Anyway, 'not to worry' I rationalised: 'this was a yacht, it was meant to be out here, this is why it was built!' This made sense and did calm me down, not that there was any reason to be anxious. Everything was working the way it was supposed to; even the sea was behaving itself. It was simply a nice, quiet, almost relaxing sail.

It was so sedate that I thought about making a cup of tea, but decided against this as my confidence level was not such that I felt able to leave the tiller for any length of time. Consequently, can of beer instead. Mind you, just to get my cigs and a can of beer required some slick body swerves into the cabin and back to the tiller before things went awry. I really didn't feel safe at all, unless I had my hands firmly on that lump of wood at the back end of the boat. There I sat for the next two, two and half hours, quietly watching the world go by, literally in this case. A cabin cruiser came within about a quarter of a mile on my port bow and this kept my interest for a while. 'When should I wave? When should I wave?' No waving, it just disappeared somewhere astern of me. All in all, this sailing business was getting a little boring.

Slowly, but surely the Whitstable lump, as I called it, came closer and finally it was on the starboard beam, (if it had been on the port beam there would have been something seriously amiss). The time was roughly four o'clock. Had I known where Whitstable was in relation to how far I'd gone and more to the point, how far I had yet to go, somehow, I don't think I would have been sat there sailing blissfully away with hardly a care in the world.

The unfortunate state of affairs was that, as far as I was concerned Whitstable, Herne Bay and even Margate were next door to each other. In a car, we are talking ten, twenty minutes to get from one to the other.

However, in an eighteen-foot six-inch yacht, towing a dinghy, it simply wasn't the same thing at all.

The facts were, that in something like three hours I had travelled eight miles at the most, nautical or otherwise, basically put, if I'd been going any slower, I would have been going backwards. They say ignorance is bliss and in my case, they were certainly right. I didn't even bother looking at my road map, wherever it was. No, I was as happy as a pig in the proverbial, a pig wallowing in it, just outside the slaughterhouse.

Five o'clock came and went. It was getting dark and it was also getting a bit breezy... By that stage I was beginning to have a few doubts. Should I keep on my present course? ...Should I turn back? However, in reality, there was no turning back. The wind was coming from the stern; I would have had big problems turning around and it would certainly have been heavy going sailing into the wind.

It didn't really make much difference where I was, or indeed that my yacht was going so slowly. There was only one objective by that late stage in the day and that was to get to Sandwich Bay and that would take as long as it took. As long as we were moving forward and in roughly the right direction, nothing else really mattered. Well, that's the way I looked at it. Probably not terribly professional, but was I wet? Was I sinking? Was I steering into danger? Two out of three wasn't bad.

Six o'clock: it was pitch black now, a good force four blowing from the west. The conditions weren't horrendous by any means. It wasn't even particularly cold, but then I did have my yellow padded luminous jacket on and I was actually wearing my life jacket. I'd had the presence of mind to put the life jacket on shortly after leaving Oare Creek estuary; I thought that was pretty sensible, for me.

My only slight worry was that the yacht was, once more, moving further away from the land than I would have liked. This was not a major issue: it was a lot better to be swept away from the land rather than towards it, especially if the shore line happened to be dotted with outcrops of rocks. Of course, not having a chart, I didn't know if there were any rocks inshore or not, but I wasn't too keen to find out. All I did to correct this leeway was to steer more to starboard. If the worse came to the worse, I would have to do a gybe, which wasn't a worry, as I had already made one of these earlier in the day, so fully proficient in the techniques of gybing. I had purposely practised this manoeuvre, because I had read somewhere that gybing your yacht could get a bit hairy, if not done properly. Consequently, being the circumspect chappy that I was, I gave it a go and as the book had said: 'performing a gybe is perfectly safe as long as everything is carried out under control.' As it turned out, when I'd given this a try in the afternoon, everything was under control and the boat had come around to starboard, ninety degrees to the original course, no problem at all. In fact, I had to gybe to get back on course, so in reality, I had made two gybes. As I say, fully proficient in the all aspects of gybing and after only two gybes. Popeye eat your heart out.

My confidence was somewhat misguided, because, if the truth were known, I hadn't practiced any gybes at all. I thought I had. A gybe takes place when the sail travels from one side of the boat to the other and this had not happened in my earlier efforts. All I had really done was alter course...

It was dark out there, but I always had the shore lights for company, the visibility was good. Amongst all of these lights, one set began to hold my attention more and more. The boat grew ever so slowly nearer to these and it became obvious they were showing green, white, green in a vertical line. They were harbour lights. "Bloody hell, mate! I could pop in there..." It had to be Herne Bay; I didn't even know Herne Bay had a harbour (I didn't have a chart...) There it was though, no question, green, white, green, port entry light, telling me I had permission to enter the harbour.

Never mind any of that, I could rest up for the night, get ashore have a few beers, good night's kip and start afresh at dawn.

This sounded like an extremely good idea to me. The weather wasn't brilliant and to be honest, stuck out in the middle of the North Sea in the dead of night, all on your own, was not a bundle of fun. Decision made, all that remained for me to do was get my little yacht through the harbour entrance. This would entail a gybe to starboard, but as I had practiced doing this twice, earlier in the day, I didn't have any worries... Because as we all know, I was now fully proficient in the art of gybing or not, as the case may be.

The wind had veered slightly to the northwest at some point in the late afternoon, I wasn't quite sure when. This had caused me to set the sails on the starboard side and although I didn't know it, this was in actual fact my one and only gybe, although as far as I was concerned it was my third. The real gybe, if that indeed was what it was, didn't involve messing around with the bit of wood stuck on the back end, so it was that much simpler. I could do simple, simple was easy.

This sailing lark was a little like life itself, keep everything under control and you won't go far wrong, might not go very far, but you won't be wrong. Bit of homespun philosophy for you, I don't think Nietzsche will lose any sleep over my pearls of wisdom. Mind you, he has been dead for about a hundred years, so not really too bothered about anything.

Gybe number 'four' coming up, just as before I had lowered the jib, or furled it in to be more accurate, it saved me playing about with two sails when doing this awkward gybe stuff. I began hauling on the sheets to tighten up the mainsail, bringing it in towards the centre of the boat. When it was in the region of twenty-five degrees to the centre line, I shoved the tiller over to bring the yacht round to starboard. - Bang! ... Crack! - "What the hell was that!?"

The whole boat vibrated violently, then she began to heel over and in less than a second the yacht was almost on her side.

'Bloody Hell! ... We're going over!...'

As we had started to turn, the mainsail had been taken by the wind and flew across to the port side. It reached the end of its travel, with a jarring crash. The wind had caught the sail even more, as by then we were turning sideways on to this force four north-westerly and this just blew us further and further over like we weren't even there.

I had difficulty staying on my feet and for a split-second I thought I was going in the water. The boat must have gone over fifty, sixty degrees, more...

Kettles, cups and cans of beer went smashing around on the inside of the cabin, the least of my worries.

Now Solo was virtually broadside onto the wind, it was worse than ever, howling and whistling noises in the rigging and in my ears, every gust tried to blow me off the deck.

I grabbed at the air, trying frantically to find the rope for the self-release mechanism for the boom. At the third attempt, I caught it and pulled hard. The boom and the mainsail once released were taken by the wind with a vengeance, the whole yacht vibrated again, as the boom crashed to a stop against the mast. 'That won't have done it much good...' At least the wind had gone out of the sail.

The yacht was leaning to port at an alarming angle and that's where it stayed for... Well forever...

'It's not going to come back up...'

I watched and waited; I couldn't believe how far the thing was over: 'This is not good...'

The sail was flapping wildly, whiplash sounds cracking every second. Even through all the sounds of the wind and the sail, I could still hear my breathing. It was hard and loud and desperate.

Somewhere along the way, I did try to bring the boat back to port, to ease the situation, but after I had let go the mainsail, basically I was rooted to the spot, watching the mast, just waiting for it to go one way or the other. Waiting to find out if I was going to live or die...

Finally, and oh so slowly, she did decide to return to something approaching the upright.

During all of this time, probably only five or six seconds in real time, I just stood there as best I could, I was in total disbelief that this could have happened. It was the speed at which it had all taken place that terrified me more than anything. There was no chance to react... Events took place so fast, that I was simply overwhelmed...

The second the mast started to move away from the water, rather than go the other way, I have to say, there was one seriously relieved little sailor stuck out on the dark waves that night. I hoped and prayed the worst of it was over, but surely some damage must have been done…

What had gone wrong anyway, one second everything was fine, the next all hell had broken loose. The only saving grace was that the boom hadn't taken my head off as it swung from one side of the boat to the other. Then again, I was keeping my head down; I knew the boom was going to travel to the other side. I just didn't realise how savagely this was going to take place, especially as I had hauled the sheets in to stop any uncontrolled gybe. Obviously, I'd made some kind of miscalculation. And boy, that was a spectacular miscalculation.

I couldn't believe my luck, there didn't appear to be any permanent damage. There might not have been any serious damage to the boat, but there had been some serious damage to my health, not to mention my confidence.

Solo was sailing okay, leaning over a bit, but nothing too drastic and all her bits and pieces seemed to be intact. Considering the noise of the boom and all the juddering which had taken place, I was amazed that there wasn't anything bent or broken. Amazed and relieved yes, but also badly shaken. I was a good half-mile out from the shore and if the boat floundered there, then I'd go down with it. When this thought filtered into my brain, I suddenly felt very cold... Very cold and very alone...

I steadied the boat, trimmed the sail and headed directly for the harbour entrance. The yacht's motion, now I'd altered course, was a lot more uncomfortable, but given the traumatic experience I had just been through and the fact that I was heading in, the rocking of the boat was a minor consideration. I was just happy to be afloat.

I wasn't out of the woods yet, I still had to get my yacht into the harbour through the pier heads and with the wind blowing the way it was, across the entrance and at a brisk force four, that was not going to be easy. My plan of action was to get something like a hundred yards off the pier heads, then start up the engine and go through into the harbour under power. For some unknown reason, my confidence in my sailing ability had taken a bit of a nose dive.

As I came closer to the pier heads, I could see that the two pillars guarding the entrance were solid lumps of stone, standing thirty feet or more out of the water, or to put it more graphically, if I hit either of those, they would be picking up bits of plastic from the shoreline for weeks.

The waves were lapping around the base of the pier heads fairly vigorously, the wind catching the waves and tossing spray in all directions. This was a good indicator that some degree of caution would be required to traverse through to the safety of the harbour. Then again, there had to have been seventy-five yards between the piers, surely, not even I could miss an entrance that size.

I took about fifteen to twenty minutes to get to within my hundred yards to the entrance. This time, at least, gave me a chance to calm down from my previous mishap and also, to take stock of the boat, which did appear to be performing well, with no long term affects from my disastrous gybe. Once in position (a hundred yards to the west), the first thing would be to start the engine, which I did with no problem. I had deliberately aimed to the west of the harbour, as I knew that it would take a time to get the mainsail down and with luck, by the time I had the sail down and wrapped around the boom, we would have drifted to the harbour entrance. That was the theory, lovely little theory. Unfortunately, it took so long to get the bloody sail down and tied up around the boom that I had drifted past the pier heads by over a hundred yards. In essence, I had actually missed the harbour entrance...

From that position, a hundred yards to the east of the entrance, I had to power against the wind and tide and there were a few moments when I wasn't sure whether the boat was making any head way or not. It must have taken at least twenty minutes to travel those hundred yards back to the stone edifices at the harbour's opening. Nevertheless, we did make it. God knows what might have happened if the engine had packed up.

I was very grateful, to turn into the harbour, through the pier heads, where the wind and waves simply died away.

"Thank God! For that..." I murmured intensely. The last forty-five minutes could have gone a little better...

Herne Bay harbour despite the fact of those two massive pillars at its entrance, wasn't particularly big, nor was it particularly busy. In fact, only two other boats appeared to be in the entire harbour. I didn't care how big the place was, or how busy, it was calm and that would do for me.

At the eastern end of the harbour, the harbour was long and narrow, there seemed to be a slipway. It was dark, but the street lights from the main road, which was only a couple of hundred yards away, gave out plenty of light, so I could see where to go fairly easily. I trundled towards the slipway, past the anchored little yacht similar to mine and a cabin cruiser, the idea being to get as near to the concrete slipway as possible, drop the anchor and then use my dinghy to get ashore. As I sailed up to the jetty, I now saw that there were several other boats on the beach. I say beach, whether it was due to the glow of the street lamps or not, I didn't know, but it looked awfully shiny to me. I had a sneaking suspicion that this was mud and lots of it, hence the use of the nice solid concrete slipway for my sojourn ashore.

I was feeling a lot more relaxed now that I was out of the worst of the wind and waves. Plus, using the engine was a big thing, something more predictable than the vagaries of bits of canvas flapping in the breeze. I was fairly sure the engine was not going to jump up and bite me on the backside. The way I was feeling, not something I could say the same about the mast, the sails, or the boom.

Herne Bay harbour was, as it happened, a very nice little harbour. Lovely big solid, twenty-foot-high sea wall most of the way round it, jetty at the one end, probably even had some sand further up the beach. Admittedly it wasn't the place for a super tanker, it was long enough: from the west entrance to the eastern end and the slipway, something like a third of a mile, but it was only about a hundred yards wide. Then again, it was pretty neigh low water, although not as low as it was going to get, as I was to find out to my cost.

For the next half an hour I played about basically. I threw the anchor over once, then decided that I was too near the sea wall, so I pulled it up and moved Solo about three feet, before dropping the pick again. Then I fiddled and fussed with the mainsail, I suppose it was breezy and it may have come loose and started flapping all over the place. Okay, so the cabin required a good tidy, but as for the rest of the time I was just doing things for the sake of doing them, may have been nervous energy or maybe acting for the 'crowds of people' ashore. For some reason, I was just fiddling around aimlessly.

A few people were indeed walking around, not many, bearing in mind it was eight o'clock on a blustery late September's night. 'Hey, look at me, I'm on my yacht, making everything ship shape, I'm this intrepid navigator; sailed all the way from Faversham. Hey man! I got to be the coolest thing since diced carrots...'

I'm sure I must have been a curio to the natives, whether they thought I was a super-hero or not was very dubious. 'What is that idiot doing?' Would probably have been more like it?

I know, if I had been walking my dog along the sea wall on a cold, damp, wintry night and I saw some person (for the want of a better word) steaming through the pier heads in an eighteen-foot yacht, I somehow don't think I would be saying to myself:

'Oh what a wonderful clever little person we have here...'

It's just a shame I didn't have the perspicacity to place myself in the mind of the dog walker. This might have made me re-think the whole venture, especially when you consider that the sea had already had a bash at trying to kill me and I still had a very long way to go.

A little perspicacity would have come in handy; a crystal ball would have been a lot better.

If I could have seen the future, I would have left the boat there that night... And in no way, would I have returned...

Chapter Five

Shore Leave
(Should have stayed at Home)

I ended up ashore without getting wet, amazingly. Climbing into the dinghy proved to be a bit on the wobbly side, but once in, I found rowing across the fifty yards to the slipway was quite good fun. The fact that I was off the death trap might have had something to do with my improved mood.

No sooner had I got out of the rowing boat than I was accosted by, what I can only describe as an urchin. A young lad of about thirteen, who acted more like he was thirty rather than his real age.

"Oh! You can put your boat here; it'll be safe enough." He informed me chirpily. I dragged the dinghy out of the water and placed it to the side of the concrete jetty.

"There's usually a charge for staying in the harbour, you know…"

"No, I didn't know." Aye Aye, what's this little tyke up to?' I thought to myself.

"I could take the money if you like?" He said innocently. I thought for a second he was going to put his hand out for me to pay him on the spot.

"So, you're the harbour master then are you?" I asked, some irritation creeping into my voice.

"Oh no, he lives up there," the urchin pointed to somewhere in the middle of Herne Bay: "But he's not there at the moment. I'm just looking after things for him."

"Oh good. Nice to see the place is in such good hands... Best if I pay him, don't you think? Then everyone knows what's what... But, when I see him, I will tell him how helpful you were..."

"Ok..." The wind had gone out of his sails now he thought the real harbour master might find out what he had been up to.

"Right I'm off to make a phone call, be back in a short while." This wasn't strictly true, but I didn't entirely trust this young entrepreneur. If he knew I was going for a few pints, I had visions of him, small as he was, running off with my dinghy.

I turned and started to walk away.

"I'll go and see if I can find him then..." He shouted after me.

"That's a good idea..." I said over my shoulder and continued under my breath, "and while you're at it, get lost..." Maybe he was just trying to be helpful, who knows? Anyway, never saw him again, or the harbour master for that matter.

I wandered up to the main road in search of a pub. As it happens, there was one almost opposite the road to the slipway. Despite the desperate need for alcohol. The road I was walking along ran parallel too and was higher than the port, such as it was. From that elevated vantage point, there was a good view of the harbour and of course, my little baby.

I just had to take a stroll along the main road and look down at my pride and joy. I could say this now; now I wasn't being tossed around on the ocean waves like so much churned up flotsam.

It would be true to say, I did feel a certain amount of pride, she was looking quite serene in the glow from the street lights with only slight movement of her bows as she lay at anchor. I wanted to stop people and say: 'Hey look down there! That's my yacht.' Fortunately, there was no one around, on my side of the road at any rate. I walked along for a couple of hundred yards, admiring Solo, no doubt with a silly smirk on my face. I was in self-indulgent mode, and why not?

Slowly but surely my mind turned to more important matters: alcohol and as chance would have it, on the next street corner was a pub. I crossed the road, nearly getting run down. Obviously, after being at sea for such a long voyage, it was going to take me some time to get used to traffic and the like.

It wasn't the greatest pub in the world, I have to say and once inside, yes, I had just landed from Faversham, but I got the distinct impression the locals thought I had landed from Mars.

Still, the barmaid, whom I would not have liked to have picked a fight with by the way, did acknowledge my presence with a welcoming growl. I got my beer and was pleased to see that after receiving my change I still had all my fingers. I found a corner somewhere, sat down, had a cigarette (the good old days when you could) with the beer and contemplated the day's proceedings.

I had to admit that everything hadn't gone completely according to plan, for one thing I should have been supping a pint in Sandwich by that stage, not in Herne bloody Bay.

It wasn't until I phoned the wife that a degree of understanding of how little a distance I had actually travelled began to sink home.

"Well, where are you...? She demanded

"Herne Bay..."

"Herne Bay!!! Is that all?... You've got miles to go..."

"Have I? Oh well... Where's Herne Bay then? It's about half way isn't it...?

"Half way, you're joking, aren't you? It's probably not even a quarter..."

"Oh dear, I suppose I'll see you tomorrow then..."

"At the rate you're going, I'm not so sure..."

That was more or less the whole conversation, I did ask about the weather, wet and windy was her reply. Mind you, I think I could have told her that.

Sitting back down with my pint, I said to myself: 'Oh well, not to worry'... I still didn't really know where Herne Bay was...

I popped into another couple of pubs. They were an improvement on the first, then that wasn't difficult. In the last pub, I ended up talking to this bloke about how wonderful the nightlife was in Herne Bay. I'd have to take his word for that. Then, after telling me how good Herne Bay was, he said he preferred Faversham.

"And how far away is Faversham anyway?" I enquired, almost casually.

"Oh! About two minutes down the road..." That kind of finished me off. I'd been to Herne Bay, had me three pints, time to move on.

I was being a sensible old salt: drinking and driving was bad enough, but drinking and sailing a yacht was in point of fact a lot worse, at least for one's own safety. No, it was time to hit the water... Literally, as things transpired.

I found my dinghy; the urchin had not half inched it after all. The tide had gone down quite away and I had to drag the boat about twenty feet to the water's edge. I suppose I should have realised then, that I might have a problem on my hands.

 At the water, the rowboat floated okay. I gave it a shove and jumped in. The dinghy stopped dead...

'Oooh Dear! That wasn't meant to happen.'

With my extra weight, there was not enough water below us to stay afloat. After a fair bit of pushing on the oar, using it like a punt and rocking the tender back and forward, I did manage to get the boat into deeper water. Here I could use the oars the way they were designed to be used.

'Thank God for that!' I heaved a sigh of relief. Thirty or forty feet further on, I was back to square one; in the same boat. Whatever... Stuck!

Sometime later, ten, twenty minutes later, I don't know, by one means or another, I had managed to get the dinghy within twenty-five feet of Solo, but that was as far as she was going. Despite everything I did, it refused to budge. The situation was so dire, I hadn't given a thought to whether anyone was watching from shore or not. Luckily, I don't think anyone could have been, otherwise I'm sure the RNLI inshore lifeboat would have been charging through the pier heads, shortly followed by the local press. I could see the headlines:

'Idiot Stuck in Mud,' 'Idiot left High and Dry,' 'Idiot can't read Tide Tables.' The operative word being 'Idiot!'

Two choices: I could stay with the dinghy until it began to float, two, three hours, God knows how long? I certainly didn't (no tide tables with me#!!). Or I could jump into the water and drag the piece of garbage the last twenty-five feet to my yacht.

It was cold, it had started to rain and after all my exertions trying to get the dinghy to the boat I was knackered. There wasn't any decision to make really. At this point, I did look around to see if anybody was watching, not a soul. Off came the shoes and socks and off with the jeans as well. It wasn't the time for false modesty. If I was going to do this, then let's do it quickly was my opinion. Unfortunately, my almost new trainers would have to go back on, there was no way of telling what I might have stood on once in the water. In the same vain, I had no idea how deep the mud was going to be on the bottom, could have been six-foot-deep for all I knew. I put one foot over the side, leaning heavily into the boat just in case my foot and the rest of me, for that matter, disappeared below the waves without trace. The trainers went into the sea about six inches, then it hit the squelchy stuff, it went down and down and down, got to have been two feet... Six inches of water, two feet of mud... Great!

It was messy and awkward, a bit like walking knee deep through snow, except that it made extremely revolting noises every time you lifted your foot out of the water. It was also a different colour to snow and had a peculiar odour. In fact, it was nothing like walking in snow. It was a lot more like walking in, you know what.

Once the weight was off the dinghy, she floated no bother at all and it didn't take too long to get to the yacht. It was cold and horrible, but I suppose it wasn't that much of a hassle. The hassle started once back on-board Solo.

I was covered in it, it was more like clay than mud and it stuck to everything, especially the hairs on my legs. It took nearly half an hour to clean the mess. The stuff wasn't only on me; it had ended up all over the cockpit of the boat. By the time I was finished I was thoroughly fed up, I could have done with going ashore for a few more pints. Somehow, I couldn't see that happening. The best I could console myself with was a can of beer and a clean pair of socks. At least I had had the common sense to bring along some extra cloths, in case of emergencies. The way things were going I was beginning to feel maybe I should have brought my whole wardrobe.

I snuggled under the blankets and with the cabin hatch all shut up and the heat from the gaslight, it was all pretty cosy in there. I had my radio for company and tried to find some station giving out the weather forecast, but only managed to get one of those phone-in programs. The DJ was slagging off the punters left right and centre. It was funny at first, but became a drag after a while. I twiddled the dial trying to get radio four, I knew the forecast would be on at three minutes to the hour or was it three minutes past the hour. It didn't matter, because I couldn't find the station anyway.

I looked at my clock: 10.42. I switched everything off and I should imagine by 10.43, I was fast asleep, most unusual for me. It was true what they said about the sea air: gave you an appetite and made you look forward to hitting the sack.

That was me for the night, or so I thought. It was not to be...

Chapter Six

The Second Leg
(Herne Bay to Dawn)

Around about one thirty in the morning the tide had come in and had started to rock the boat. I don't know if it was the boat moving that awoke me, or whether the sound of the sea lapping against the hull that did the job, but something did... And I just knew, I wasn't going to get anymore sleep that night.

I lay there for a while, wondering what to do. Underneath the blankets most of me was nice and warm. My feet however, must have been sticking out of the end, because they were frozen. I shuffled around trying to warm them up. The next problem, which came to mind, was not quite so easy to rectify. The beer from the previous evening was having its effect on my bladder. Nothing else for it, I would have to leave the relative warmth of my bunk and go and face the cold night air. There was a loo in the cabin, but as far as I was concerned, this was for extreme emergencies only. Besides I had a perfectly good toilet outside. It was called Herne Bay harbour. I steeled myself for the ordeal and threw the covers off. As I had guessed, it was pretty bloody cold outside and just to make matters worse, I had to take my socks off. I didn't have a spare pair of shoes and I wasn't going to put my sodden trainers on until absolutely necessary. Every cloud has a silver lining, I suppose. Balancing at the stern of the boat, urinating into the harbour was quite a relief.

The wind seemed to have died down. The noises coming from the rigging were a lot less angry than they had been before. The drizzle had cleared away and although it was still a bit breezy, the conditions, it appeared to me, were fairly favourable for a spot of sailing. Then again, the conditions in the confines of the harbour walls were one thing. The state of the wind and sea on the other side of that wall could be vastly different.

I returned to the cabin. Sitting on my bunk doing a lot of sighing and trying to keep warm. I soon realised that the fun had gone out of my little yachting trip. I wasn't going to go back to sleep, it was pointless just sitting there feeling cold, damp and miserable.

I was more than a bit concerned about taking the boat out through the pier heads in the dead of night. Going to sea in the wee small hours had not been part of the plan. I had a torch and that was all that we required for my size of vessel, so we were legal. Legal or not, the whole idea was far from ideal. Sadly, the alternative was to sit there and stare at the clouds of breath coming out of my mouth for the next four or five hours.

In the end, I decided I would take her out, but only to have a look. No putting up sails, just use the engine and if the sea was too choppy or it looked a bit iff'y in anyway, I would turn around and return to the safety of the harbour. Seemed to make sense to me.

That was the plan of action. I thought about making a cup of tea, but said: 'Sod it! Let's get on with it.' It was an all-weather job, yellow jacket, life jacket, balaclava and wet soggy training shoes; they were never going to be the same again.

I fired up the engine. I'd already topped her up with petrol, which was one less job to worry about. Then I had to raise the anchor, this proved more difficult than expected and at one point, I thought the thing was never going to break loose at all, but with one last, almighty tug I managed to free it. The fact that I'd had difficulty with the anchor, should not have been a surprise. After all, I'd experienced the mud of the harbour bottom, first hand, not three hours earlier.

Everything was set. I put the engine in gear, revved her up and we were on our way again. It was two o'clock of this October morning, we were only slightly behind schedule... about fourteen hours, that's all.

I said goodbye to the other two boats at anchor as I passed them, not sure why, but there you are.

A couple of minutes later and I was passing through the pier heads of Herne Bay harbour. I wasn't sorry to leave the place; my little stopover had not entirely been a bundle of fun. On the other hand, standing in the cockpit, staring out to sea, it all looked very bleak, very cold, and very empty out there...

The engine rattled its way straight out from the entrance, maybe two hundred yards; the sea state wasn't that bad, three-foot waves at the most, only one or two white horses, which meant a force three... The conditions were good.

Should I continue? ... I turned to starboard and once Solo was pointing in the right direction, roughly due east, I pulled on the sheets to raise the foresail... I don't think I made a conscious decision to keep on going, it just sort of happened.

Switching the engine off, as before, was a fait accompli. This time I didn't have any qualms about it. The yacht was steady and so without any hesitation on my part, I leant down and pressed the button, the engine went silent...

So, we sailed for half an hour or more. It was cold and blustery and a little rough, but nothing too scary. I had made my mind up, I was not going to set the mainsail, slow and steady was the order of the day. Apart from anything else, I would have had to have clamber onto the roof of the boat to get the main up and anyway, at the time, we were sailing without a problem...

...That was during the first half hour...

Then the wind began to pick up, this increased my anxiety level a few notches, but no more than that. The wind was slightly on the starboard quarter, so we were running more or less with the wind, which suited me just fine.

However, when the swell began to increase. That was a different story. I didn't really know when waves changed from being waves into being a swell. All I knew was that the three-foot waves hitting the stern, had hardly caused any effect on the motion of the boat... Now, something had changed...

The waves or swell, were hitting the back of the yacht and lifting her up and as the wave continued moving passed, the front end would rise, we were pitching in other words. I think it's fair to say I wasn't overly anxious. It's also true to say, I wasn't particularly happy either.

We were speeding up, then slowing down, speeding up, slowing down... Not an uncomfortable motion. It's the kind of thing that you would expect to get in a yacht that size, but there were a few nagging doubts beginning to form in the back of my mind.

That's the trouble with the sea: she was so sneaky. One minute, there you are sailing away quite merrily, not a care in the world (that might have been a slight exaggeration) the next you're in a howling, raging storm... And that wasn't too far from the truth.

I'm sure there must have been some warning signs, the sea must have picked up gradually, but I didn't notice it. I had seen the white horses increase in number, so I knew the wind had got up and yes, that would affect the waves, but that couldn't explain the amount of buffeting we were taking.

It was a swell, that had come in from somewhere, I was sure of it. How it had developed or where it had come from was not the issue, the effect on my yacht was.

These heaving waves causing me to bob up and down, as if connected to some kind of giant slow-moving spring. They had a period you could measure in metres. From crest to crest was way longer than my boat... Okay! All waves had periods, but for me, a period of a wave was like a couple of feet... The distance between the crests of these things coming at me was ten metres or more, and they weren't getting any smaller either...

This was a decided failing of mine: I kind of knew about stuff, but didn't really understand the implications of what was taking place... At that juncture in time, it was probably just as well...

Things were beginning to look a bit grim.

I could not have turned around and headed back to Herne Bay. It was the same problem as the day before. Just didn't have the experience to beat into the wind, certainly not in those conditions. And anyway, the last thing I wanted was to be sideways on to that sea. I wondered whether to lower the foresail, it was taking a bit of a battering, especially as we were speeding up and slowing down. As we sped up the sail lost the wind and as we came out of a trough and slowed down the sail caught the wind again, more often than not with an alarming great 'Crack!' Rightly or wrongly, despite all the noises, I decided that the yacht was riding the swell pretty well, all things considered, and any change in the overall speed of the vessel may well put her in jeopardy. I left well alone.

As if I didn't have enough on my mind, the dinghy I was towing, seemed to be riding the waves fairly well and that was a problem. She was riding the waves far too well; she had a tendency to do a bit of surfing. Under normal circumstances, the tender was about fifteen feet away, but when a wave picked her up, she would come charging at me and end up something like four, five feet away. It would just take an extra big wave and this thing was going to be sitting in the back of Solo. The extra weight would have lowered the stern of the yacht, with another wave coming along, the water wouldn't be rolling past, it would be crashing into the cockpit and I would be left praying for a miracle...

The dinghy was becoming a liability; there was no two-ways about it. Attacking the back end could turn out very dangerous, but along with that, the bloody thing was also virtually stopping Solo in her tracks. When the rowing boat was running down the hill of water, the tension was off the towrope, but as soon as it stopped, the tension would come back on the rope. As the dinghy reached the towrope's limit, everything on-board, including myself lurched forward. This wasn't helping the stresses and strains on the yacht and it sure as hell wasn't doing a lot for the stress and strains inside me either.

I don't think it even entered my head to cut it free, the kids and I were going to have so much fun with that little dinghy.

In the background, the wind was growling at me by now, the noise made worse by the shrill whistles as it rushed past the empty shrouds in the mast. When I turned around to check the dinghy, sea spray would hit me in the face and sting my eyes. Every time the swell struck Solo, all it seemed to want to do was push the boat sideways. I had to act quickly; it was a continual struggle with the tiller to keep the swell waves directly astern. It was a dark night and it was getting darker by the minute...

I wouldn't say panic had set in, but it wasn't far away. It wasn't far away at all...

A biggish wave went by, had to have been over five foot high, difficult to say. I was seated on the starboard side of the cockpit, fiercely gripping the tiller. I watched the wave, it was slow, ponderous in its movement, but the power and the size of it... you could feel it... This thing could snuff your life out, without even trying. The crest broke slightly as it passed, the white horses luminous in the dark. The Monster rolled on and blended into the body of the dull black night.

I thought about my daughter, I called her a monster, that was a bit of a joke. This wasn't funny... This was a real Monster... One little throw of the dice and this Monster would swallow me alive...

"What's the fuss? It's only a bit of bloody water, for Christ's sake..." I think I may have been trying to cheer myself up... I shouldn't have said it.

Not even a second... We were over! AGAIN!...

'This was bad! This was very bad!'

We had stopped dead in the water...! The boat had skewed right round to starboard and we were leaning to port sixty degrees. In the blink of an eye the yacht had come round and had broached the waves, we were sideways on to that Sea. To make matters worse (if that was possible), the wind had taken the sail and this was pushing her over yet more. She was over so much, there was no way she was coming back from this...

If I had been on the port side, I would have already been in the water. As it was, quick reactions were the only thing that saved me, I had jammed my foot against the port side seat and the floor of the cockpit, I was upright, but I was the only thing that was...

It was as if watching a film: a 'B' movie in black and white, sails flapping everywhere, wind and sea spray whirling around, howling noises, the captain lashed to the wheel, holding on for grim death. This wasn't happening to me...

I slipped the starboard sheet for the foresail off the ratchet gear. The sheet just disappeared forward somewhere. Then, with both hands I pulled the tiller towards me. If I couldn't get the boat upright, with the stern facing into the wind and the swell and do it quickly, then it was all over. One big wave that's all it was going to take...

At least I had figured out what had gone wrong, I glanced over my shoulder and sure enough that dinghy, that bloody dinghy was under water, up to its gunwales, you could barely see the thing.

It was just dead weight; it was acting like a sea anchor and by God was it effective... I had to get rid of it...

I wrapped one arm around the tiller and with my free hand tried to undo the knot...

Solo was beginning to dig herself out of the hole she was in. Once I had let go the foresail, she'd righted herself fairly quickly and seemed to be responding to the rudder. When I realised this, I believe a faint glimmer of hope entered my soul

'Jesus Christ, I'm not actually going to survive, this am I..?'

This glimmer of hope was soon well and truly extinguished. I had managed to escape one emergency, only to end up in another, and this new emergency, was one that I could do nothing about...

Oh yes! I was scared before, when the boat had suddenly keeled over, my heart was in my mouth, but I had to react quickly, I had to think quickly. There just wasn't any time to worry about how fast your heart was beating. The bottom line... Do or die...

The boat had steadied itself and in a way, this was causing more problems. The yacht wanted to move forward, but the dingy didn't.

'Look you're a hundred percent better off than you were a minute ago.' I was obviously trying to bolster some confidence in myself. It didn't work... It was about then; I heard the creaking noises coming from the transom...

'Get that bloody knot undone, for God's sake!...'

Again, I clawed at the knot with my only free hand, it was no use. There was too much weight on it. If I could somehow get both hands to it maybe that would have helped, but I just couldn't let go the tiller. The rolling grey monsters were relentlessly trying to force us sideways. The whole thing was hopeless...

'You're going to die here James...'

The stern was now face on to the swell and every time the force of the waves smashed into the yacht it tried to push us forward, but the flooded dinghy was like a brick wall and my transom was tied fast to that wall. The back of the boat was being pulled away from the rest of the yacht... And there was nothing I could do...

I looked at the knot. The rope was old and frayed and soaked through. It was a bowline; I had tied it myself: 'they weren't meant to jam.'

I watched as another wave hit; water splashed into the cockpit. I tried to pull on the rope to take the weight off. The foresail wildly flapping and cracking, wasn't making me feel any the more comfortable. But it was the creaking sound from the transom that was really getting to me. This wasn't loud, but it was terrifying none the less.

'You're going to die here James...'

Panic... I looked into the cabin there was a knife in there, where the bloody hell was it though? I had no idea; I couldn't leave the tiller anyway. I remember gritting my teeth, and with my nails tore at the knot for the umpteenth time, I wasn't doing anything, there was no way. The stern was pounded by yet another massive swell. Again, I had to pull on the tiller to keep her from broaching too.

I turned to look at the sea behind me; turned to stare into the cabin, then turned to look at the sea behind yet again... Blind Terror, I couldn't think... There was nothing I could do... I'd given up...

How long would it take, two minutes? Five minutes? ... It was just a question of time... The waves would break over the stern or the transom would give way. Either way the end result was the same... And I had time to think about it...

It was the feeling of helplessness that was the worst. There had always been options before in my life, good or bad, but there had always been something... Now, there was nothing...

The swell crashed into the transom, the creaking getting louder... It was the only thing I could hear now...

Another wave... Solo lurched forward and the stern came up sharply...

'Oh! My God! This is it!...'

I leaned backwards and tugged at the dinghy's tow rope... "Bloody hell...!"

There was nothing there... We were free...

Didn't know why and I didn't care...

I suppose I should have been elated, but I was probably in a state of shock. The fact of the matter was, that the wind was still howling around my head; the swell had grown even higher if anything; my sails were all over the place and I'd lost my dinghy. I was still in deep, deep trouble. The only grain of comfort, now that the dinghy was gone, I had a chance... Not a very good one maybe, but I'd take it nevertheless...

Talking of dinghies, I don't believe it myself, but I actually contemplated going back to collect the thing, only briefly, it should be said, but even so. I could only conclude the pressure had finally sent me over the edge and I was now quite insane.

I collected myself... The first thing to do was recover that noisy flapping foresail. I soon found this was not going to be easy. The starboard sheet, which I'd let go of as soon as the yacht had begun to flounder, had indeed disappeared forward and I mean disappeared.

There should have been a figure of eight knot in it to stop it flying half way down the deck; I don't know what had happened to it exactly. All I knew was that the bit of rope to pull the foresail out was missing. The only option left was to heave in the furling rope to stop the sail flapping in the breeze, which is exactly what I did.

Unfortunately, because the starboard sheet was out there somewhere, it had obviously become entangled around something. The foresail couldn't be furled in, not completely anyway. About a quarter of it was still whip lashing around the forestay, but it was the best I could do for the moment, at least.

My little yacht had been battered to buggery yet once more, but looking around and possibly more importantly listening, I couldn't detect anything untoward. Admittedly, there was the problem with the sail, but all things considered I think we had both come out of the ordeal pretty well. The transom, looked like it always had, no cracks in it and no weird noises from it either, which was kind of lucky, because I would not be going very far without that.

Solo was pitching and rolling heavily and it was a struggle to keep the boat on something resembling a straight course. Only one hand could be used to do anything, the other was constantly on the tiller and even then, when the swell lifted the stern, it was a case of dropping everything and grabbing the tiller with both hands. Yet I had to find out what had happened to the tender. By using various bits of my body to hold onto the towrope when we were struck by a wave, I managed to pull up the end of the rope.

All that was left of my dinghy was an eyebolt... A rusty old eyebolt and that was scary: my fate had depended on the thickness of fibreglass holding this two-inch bit of metal. If it had not given way, I would have still been a hundred yards astern, probably to remain there forever... It had just been pure luck... A cold shiver ran down my backbone.

This feeling of dread didn't last long, there was too much going on around me to dwell on what might, or might not have happened. It seemed a lifetime away, but as mad as it sounded, I would guess, from the time of the tender getting swamped to where I was at that moment, had taken no more than three or four minutes. The longest three or four minutes of my life. Even in that short time, I knew it was impossible, but I was sure the individual waves of the swell had become deeper in height.

Indeed, they did seem to be growing, almost as if alive.

Looking over to starboard, towards the land a mile away, probably more, all I could see across the expanse of water, were the white streaks of waves breaking. These were not just white horses; these were long breaking waves and lots of them... I was in a force five... and that wasn't meant to be...

I had to accept that I was condemned to the mercy of the sea, not at all happy about this, but then, it wasn't as if I had much choice in the matter. The only option open to me was to get on with sailing the vessel, one thing at a time.

Sorting the sails was uppermost in my mind. This was a yacht; surely, I should have a sail up? On the other hand, two things really: to set either sail at that stage, I would have had to leave the cockpit and that was a big No! No! The second aspect of the situation: Solo was steering okay.

As long as I kept hold of the tiller and paid one hundred percent concentration to the job, then Solo showed no signs of broaching the following sea. We were going in the right direction. The swell was going easterly and therefore so were we. It just so happened to be in the right direction for us. As for speed, certainly you needed sails for that, but to hell with it!... Staying in one piece was the priority, not winning bloody races...

In the end, all I did to the sails was pull on the port sheet of the foresail and the only reason was to try to stop the sail making all that racket. It didn't really make any difference.

That was it then; roughly three in the morning, the clock was buried in the cabin somewhere, along with everything else. From what I could see the inside of the boat looked as if it had been hit by a tidal wave, but then it had...

I was stood up in the starboard side of the cockpit, left hand firmly gripping the tiller, right hand gripping the handrail and fear gripping my heart.

The wind played its part, the sound of it gushing and whooshing endlessly in your ears, sometimes loud, sometimes dying to a whisper. But it was the swell that really scared me.

It had built to such an extent that, as I stood there, these waves lumbering past were actually above my head. That meant, this was a three-metre swell... These were big... And if the stern of your boat is only half a metre out of the water, you got problems.

It wasn't as if they were slow moving. Thousands and thousands of tons of water were charging along in one enormous mass, had to be twenty miles an hour, difficult to judge. For something that huge, they were moving at an awful speed.

It was the sheer size of them that got to you, the immense volume. All that energy and power surging past my pathetic little yacht. It's something I never want to see again as long as I live. Certainly, not when stuck inside a three-metre-long bit of flimsy plastic, a mile out to sea.

When one went by, it was as if a whole mountain was moving past you, a cold, evil mountain, no feelings in there and all it wanted to do was swallow you without trace.

If nothing else it made you realise how insignificant you really were.

Another one, almost silently, rolled past, well over my head height again. Solo was completely and utterly dwarfed by this dark mass of water. This bluey, black, sinister mass of water...

I had a bad feeling about all of this... I turned to watch for the next one...

Would they get any bigger? That was the question churning in the back of my head. I was far too frightened of the answer to ask it out right. I was amazed the waves were not coming over the back end as things stood, but if this monster of a swell grew, well...

Standing bedraggled and alone with my hand painfully holding the only friend I had out there, the tiller, all I could do was watch and wait. Usually, there would have been some comment, some words revolving around in my head, a swear word or two. There was nothing. Like the silent mountains trundling past, I had become cold and empty.

How long did it all go on for? Half hour, two hours? I don't know, I just lived from one swell to the next... Every twenty-eight seconds... I counted... it seemed longer...

The lights of Margate began to get closer. This had a calming effect on my beleaguered soul, not so much because Margate was getting closer. It was more that I was getting further away from the nightmare of the dinghy disaster.

There was no doubt that Margate was approaching, but at the same time, we seemed to be heading away from the coast a little. I tried to correct this, but only succeeded giving myself another heart attack. The swell hit the starboard quarter and immediately forced the yacht into a severe yaw. I pulled hard on the tiller for the thousandth time that night. That was the last time I tried to control the boat, other than to keep the stern end on to the vicious, uncompromising sea.

Eventually, things did calm down. No way could it have been described as good. The wind was blowing force four to five and the swell was still more than this eighteen-foot six-inch yacht was designed for, but at least the waves were not towering past me anymore. A two-metre swell maybe.

We were coming up to Margate and I gave some serious thought to going into the harbour. Despite all that had gone before, I came up with the conclusion that it was probably more dangerous to attempt to enter the harbour than to stay at sea. What with the wind and the swell, it would have been so easy for me to have missed the entrance, as big as it was and if that happened, there would be lots of nasty rocks waiting for me, just to the east. That little four horse powered engine simply wasn't man enough for the job. Besides I would only have to come back out again and I wasn't sure I would be man enough for that.

'Let's get round to Sandwich Bay for God's sake and get this disaster over with...'

So, I sailed on into the night... Drifted on into the night, would have been more accurate. I still had no sails up, but we were 'sailing' fine. I don't profess to understand it. I assumed, as the wind was so strong, it was catching the hull and the cabin and these were in effect my sails. I also suspected, since the tender had gone, Solo was more responsive to the conditions. Either way, I was doing all right and anyway, I had no intention of going onto the cabin roof to muck about with the sails in the pitch dark.

The coast went by, it was full of rocks and unforgiving waves breaking on them, I was too far out to hear them, but they were in my head nevertheless. Street lights marked my way. I searched for lights in someone's home or a car, something to remind me of my family and warmth. Just the waves and the street lights...

My only solace was a cigarette: I had managed to let go the tiller and with a lot of dashing back and forward, found the packet of cigarettes and a lighter, I didn't enjoy smoking in the open air, but it said, the situation was getting back to something approaching normality. By the same token, the possibility of grabbing the flares was now open to me and I had a long hard think about actually setting one off. In the end, I didn't. The worst had to be over...

Slowly the sky became lighter. There were only a few clouds over to the east and soon they began to glow red. Against the background of the orange tint of the sky itself, it was all quite beautiful. What was it they said? "Red sky in the morning, shepherd's warning..." 'Oh! Sod all that...' I was past caring...

Chapter Seven

The Homeward Leg
(Going Down Hill)

The wind had died and the swell, a mere metre and a half. It was a lovely, crisp, autumnal day. A beautiful day for a sail. All we needed were some sails.

It was around about six in the morning, didn't have a clue really. The last time I had seen a time piece (there were two on-board) was Herne Bay and that was an extremely long time ago.

Dawn had well and truly arrived and despite all that had taken place, I was still alive... Got to say I didn't really feel alive. I don't think I felt anything: not cold or hungry, could have done with a pair of gloves maybe, but I was just there, working on autopilot. I knew what had to be done and just went ahead and did it. If I had any feeling or emotion at all, it was bewilderment. There still didn't seem to be any words in my head, no colourful expletives, no stupid comments, just the cold dawn and the sea.

Eventually, the sun's rays must have dragged me out of my stupor... The sails were the first priority. Now that daylight had finally arrived, the problem was clear. The starboard foresail sheet had become entangled with the handrails at the bow, easy enough to sort out... If I could get up there?

I had the bright idea of tying off the tiller to try to keep Solo on a relatively straight course as I scrambled forward... It didn't work. However, even though we ended up almost sideways on to the swell and she was wallowing around like a bugger, the craft wasn't going to capsize. I was able to wrestle my way forward to sort out the foresail. While out on deck doing my Seaman Sam bit, I thought it kind of made sense to get the main up as well. Consequently, after a lot of panting and puffing and pulling at me bits and bobs, I finally raised the mainsail to the top of the mast.

Once back in the cockpit, the first thing I did was tie a dirty great figure of eight knot in the starboard sheet. That was one lesson I would never forget.

As I was in safety mode, I found myself a knife, an old kitchen knife kept on-board. I placed it on the floor just inside the cabin. From now on, I would always know where this knife was.

That was another lesson I would never forget. The number of times I had been told by salty old sea dogs: "Always keep a knife on you, you never know when you might need it," and I had gone, 'yea, yea, yea…' When in the merchant navy, I had played with radars and walky-talkies and sat-navs, what did I need a knife for? Now I knew.

I trimmed the sails and headed southeast. At long, long last, I was sailing the boat as it should be sailed. More importantly, I was also on my way home.

Sometime during the earlier hours, I had turned the corner. The swell must have followed the curve of the land at Margate and Solo and I, being basically at the mercy of the swell, had done the same. The whys and wherefores didn't interest me. All that concerned me was that I was on the last leg, the downhill leg and from here on, it was going to be plain sailing... And it was, for some of the way...

The wind was still from the west, if you wanted to get technical, I would have gone for west by north, four points abaft the beam, or as near as damn it and at a comfortable force three. The sails were set to port, granted a bit of leeway, but we could handle that. Everything was hunky dory, everything apart from me...

I just wanted it all to be over. I had more than done my bit, faced up to the big bad sea. Time to park the boat, put my feet up and have a nice cup of tea. I was so fed up I didn't even want a beer. That's how bad things were...

Two or three hours of this. I saw some other idiots float by in the distance: a big sailboat, a couple of fishermen and a coast guard cutter... 'Look! I'm over here. Quick, come and save me!' Na! I couldn't be bothered.

Broadstairs came into view. That was a nice place, pop in and have a pint...

Na! I couldn't be bothered....

Well, let's face it, when in a yacht, 'Popping in' wasn't quite like parking the car up, sticking the money in the machine and disappearing to the shops. An hour later and maybe, just maybe, you might have actually managed to navigate through the pier heads... I sailed on...

It was off Broadstairs (approx 09.00,) that I had my first little set back. First one for a couple of hours anyway. Looking over to the land, I realised it was getting kind of small. Time for a spot of tacking.

I'd never done this before, but I wasn't too bothered, I had read the books, knew the theory, I knew what I was doing... I tried not to think too much about the previous night's gybe, when exactly the same thoughts had gone through my head.

The wind, had shifted to the south west or there abouts and I suppose I was in effect on a starboard tack as things stood, course by then 180ish. Now I wanted to be on a port tack, 'cause that's what yachts did, they zig zagged all over the place. See I told you I had read the theory. All I had to do was get the boat's head through the wind and watch out for the boom trying to take your head off. No problem... Yes problem. Could I get the thing through the wind? Could I hell.

Solo came off the wind to build up speed and when I thought we were going as fast as she was going to go, I shoved the tiller hard over. The next thing I knew we were dead in the water, being pushed backwards, if anything.

The best speed I could get out of her was when the wind was on the starboard beam. This meant that when the rudder was put over, the ship's head had to travel ninety degrees to go through the wind and it just wouldn't do it. After three attempts, I gave up. My mate Peter would have been calling me all the names under the sun had he been there: 'Out on you own. Can't even tack! What a tossa. You must be barking mad.' I was beginning to wonder myself, all a little late by then...

I Switched on the engine and powered round the wind. This was far from ideal: if we were on the wrong tack and if, for any reason, the engine wouldn't start, then I was going to be in deep 'merde,' using the French here, because France was quite possibly where I would end up...

It was all a bit pointless as it turned out, because we were only on that port tack for about twenty minutes, when I simply got fed up. Steering directly towards the land, unlike when sailing along the coast, there was no appreciation of forward movement. I really did feel like I was standing still. "Sod this!" I mumbled and turned to port, with the aid of the engine of course and headed off south as before.

Soon or later Ramsgate appeared off the starboard bow, 'Oh my God! bloody ferries...'

Ramsgate wasn't a mega busy port, but it did have the occasional ten thousand tonner coming and going and this meant rules and regulations, which had to be observed. The only regulation, which would inconvenience me, was to do with the traffic lanes used by the big boys to get in and out of the port.

Obviously, no dawdling in the approach lane, but also, you had to stay a mile off the entrance. This would entail getting my chart out, finding the right buoy and aiming for it. Previously, I had just been going with the flow, as it where, not following any particular course. My navigational expertise had mainly consisted of being able to see Kent. Now, I would have to do a bit of proper navigating.

This wasn't entirely true, by the time I had turned the corner at Margate, I was steering a southerly course and although I hadn't looked at my chart up until that point, I had remembered (from the time when, oh so long ago,

I was sat in my dining room working out all those lovely calculations) that I should alter course when the North Foreland lighthouse was bearing 90 degrees. At the speed, which we were making, it wouldn't have made any difference if we'd come round to a southerly heading half an hour earlier or half an hour later. But no! I waited until the bearing was ninety. Admittedly using the boat's compass, which was inlaid onto the bulkhead, wasn't what you would call an exact science here. Nevertheless, it made me feel like I knew what I was doing, which was probably the only positive aspect of the whole operation.

From the position at North Foreland, Ramsgate had come into view. Navigating off the port would involve a little more than keeping Kent on the right-hand side of the boat. Grabbing the chart, which was just inside the cabin, on my chart table - the bit of wood plonked on top of the toilet. On this scruffy old bit of paper, I had already marked two of the buoys. They didn't seem to be named, but they were the first two of a set of channel marking buoys for the approaches to Ramsgate. They were easy to identify.

Peering between sails and the cabin roof, blow me the bloody things were almost dead ahead.

The buoys were a good bit in the distance, nonetheless, there they were. The visibility was excellent, so all I had to do was keep to the outside of these, which meant keeping them on the starboard bow and I was laughing. I didn't actually feel like laughing, but my spirits had definitely taken a turn for the better.

"Don't tell me something is going right for a change."

My mood was further improved, while creeping up on Ramsgate, because not only could I see Sandwich Bay, but it gave me my first glimpse of Pegwell Bay. It was here that my voyage officially ended. It was marked on my chart 'EOP,' so it had to be true.

Even more than that, Richborough power station was clearly in view. The power station was, as near as damn it (especially at that distance) built at the entrance to the river Stour. Once I had those cooling towers hovering over my head, I was home and dry... 'I was almost there!'

I would have been almost there, if only I could have sailed as the crow flies.

Firstly, I've never seen a crow fly straight yet and secondly, I was in yacht and I've never seen one of them go in a straight line either, certainly not one I was in control of.

The two buoys at least gave me something to aim for and this made all the difference, I could see them getting closer, okay it was taking forever, but it did make it seem as if, finally, I was getting somewhere. One minute, they were no more than a speck on the horizon, then sometime down the road they were no more than a speck on the horizon. Maybe an hour later they started to get a little bigger...

It probably did take an hour, from the initial sighting of these buoys to being abreast of the first of them. In the event, I passed within about twenty feet of these channel markers. I scooted across the approach lane and amazingly enough, no ferry appeared out of thin air to run me down.

At the second buoy, on my chart, it said course 260(M)x3'. It would have been very nice to be able to take that course and end up under the power station, a meagre three miles away, but somehow, I didn't think so. I'm afraid I just wasn't that good.

I had two choices: I could do lots of little zig zags, stopping and starting the engine every five minutes, or I could do one big zig zag. I suppose really, it would just be a zig, or would it be a zag… In other words, head well south of the power station, then do the tacking business and from there on, it would be a straight run in to the river Stour.

The second course of action would entail starting the engine only the once and that's what I plumped for. My biggest fear was being stuck out there without an engine. Had I had the common sense to switch the radio on (it wasn't as if I was rushed off my feet, sat there on the back end as I was) and listened to the weather forecast, I may well have come to a different conclusion…

I didn't want to go too far away from the land. Unfortunately, Solo would only sail at an angle of forty-five degrees to the wind or more. Anything less and we just stalled. In truth, when sailing into the wind the only time you picked up any speed was when the wind was on the beam. Consequently, with a south-westerly blowing, if we wanted to maintain any reasonable rate of knots at all, you had to sail more or less south-east, wasn't too keen on this. Firstly, this course was taking us further away from the land. Secondly, if we maintained that SE'ly heading for any length of time, we would indeed be on our way to the continent.

I'd had a comfortable mornings sail and if it wasn't for my state of mind, the experience may well have been enjoyable. As the day was wearing on, (ten thirty-three as I cleared the approach lane) and sailing ninety degrees to my desired course, heading out to sea. That familiar knotted feeling in the pit of my stomach began to re-emerge.

Nothing else for it, time for a can of beer, my penultimate can which was worrying in itself. Come to that, all my supplies were running a bit low. The sandwiches gone, cheese and onion sandwiches for breakfast, very nice. There was a can of soup somewhere, but I couldn't see me lighting up the cooker, not out there. So, can of beer it was.

I reckon I was on a course of 170 degrees, south by east, give or take. It was a case of trying to keep the speed up without taking the scenic route via Ostend and amazingly enough, we seemed to be making quite good progress.

In the distance, I could see a buoy. There were several of them dotted around as it happened, but after a serious look at the chart and with the aid of a pin and a blindfold, I came to the unerring conclusion that I was heading for the 'Brake' buoy.

There were two other buoys on route to the Brake, I could see these clearly. One thing and another, I was fairly confident I knew my position, which is always quite helpful when floating on the ocean waves.

Also, further in the distance again, was yet another buoy. This was a cardinal buoy, couldn't make out whether it was north, south, east or west, but according to my chart, you had this Brake buoy and behind that was a 'Keep West' cardinal buoy. Either way, these things were becoming more and more into view. I was undoubtedly making way through the water, not a clue in the world at what rate of knots and I didn't really care. As long as there was some kind of wake behind me, that was good enough.

The next question on the agenda: when should I come round to starboard and start heading in? 'Start Heading In.' These words, music to my troubled digestive system...

It must have been eleven or thereabouts, I had just passed another buoy. Richborough power station was to the west, virtually on the starboard beam.

'Let's give it a go...'

I threw the tiller to port, to bring her into the wind, two seconds later... I was going astern. Stalled... Got the thing back on course, tried to build up some speed... Threw the tiller over again, let go the port sheet for the jib... Three seconds later... Going backwards. Back on course, sixty degrees off the wind, picking up speed... Third time lucky, no way Pedro... All I was doing was hitting a wall of wind and getting nowhere fast.

I decided on a new course of action: come around to port and put the stern through the wind. I came about one eighty degrees okay, but that was it... Heading back to bleeding Ramsgate... Solo stubbornly refused to go through the wind, end of story...

I came back round to starboard and resumed my original course and had a little think... Seriously pee'd off and in that frame of mind, the term 'pissing in the wind' came to mind and despite my best intellectual endeavours: 'Pissing in the wind,' was all I came up with.

I gave up my frustrating attempts at tacking and for the time being continued to head for my buoys.

The fact is, Solo had all its weight at the back end and due to this she was never going to carry enough angular momentum to get the head through the wind. It was all a bit technical; an experienced sailor would have known... It wasn't a total waste of time and effort. My feeble attempts at controlling this stupid piece of fibreglass, made me realise my inadequacies. I was never going to be in the same league as Horatio Nelson and the best I could hope for was to get this sad excuse for a sailor, somewhere near a piece of land, so as I could scramble ashore. Dignity in tatters maybe, but with lungs full of air, not water...

Sometime this side of eternity, the Brake buoy came into reach, about thirty feet away. It always surprised me how big these things were when you got close, probably because they looked so small when you first saw them, almost like toys bouncing around in the distance. This one was just a big can, (a silent can, it had to be said, it should have had a bell on it, either I was going deaf or it had lost its tinkle,) dirty red in colour with rusty white letters 'BRAKE' marked on it, least I'd got that right...

I wondered whether to start the engine and head for the power station, but in one of my few rational moments, I came to the conclusion that: better to go further south. This would give me room to manoeuvre. I could always sail away from the south westerly and come to the north easy enough. However, if I found I was drifting north of Richborough, beating back on course was not going to be too much fun, especially with my forlorn abilities. I sailed on to the cardinal buoy.

The conditions were good; I would have said it was still blowing from the southwest and no more than a three. The sunshine was out, as it had been all day. For the first of October it was a lovely, warm and almost pleasant afternoon.

If I had been sitting in the Admiral Owen, a pint in hand, talking to my mates, I would have probably said something silly like: 'Imagine sitting in a wee yacht out in Sandwich Bay on a day like this, wouldn't that be brilliant.' Well, I was there and it wasn't brilliant, it was a pain in the backside.

The next buoy the black, yellow, black 'North West Goodwin' (for some reason the word Goodwin sent a chill through me of its own accord) came up within the space of twenty minutes. The two buoys had not been too far apart, and I wasn't going deaf. This one's bell was 'donging' away merrily.

It was now or never... I pulled the cord for the engine... It didn't start... "Oh my God!..." Tried it for a second time, still didn't start. Funny things were happening in my chest, "Bloody

Hell, I'm five miles out here..." The palpitations increased...

I stopped for a second and looked at the NW Goodwin. Could I throw a rope to it? ... I pulled the engine rope for a third time... The engine fired, I dived for the accelerator handle and turned the revs up... The weird feeling in my chest cavity slowly went away.

I let go the port sheet and tightened up the main sail, put the rudder over and came to starboard. Solo's head went through the wind as sweet as a nut. I set both sails on the starboard side, eyed up Richborough Power Station and set course directly for those beautiful concrete towers.

The sails filled out, I heaved on the ropes to stop any luffing and cut the engine. Silence ensued, apart from the bells, the waves hitting the hull, the breeze in the rigging and the occasional sound of breaking wind.

The true wind was just forward of the port beam and Solo was cutting her way through the water nicely, the satisfying sounds of the bow repeatedly smashing into the waves was testimony to this. Everything was right with the world and after all this time, I was now actually heading in towards land.

Straight run. Yes, it would take a bit of time, but all I had to do was keep the towers in line with the bows and I would literally be home and dry. The power station was so far away it was little more than a grey, amorphous blob, barely rising above the even greyer land. It was miles away, I knew, but I also knew, that just like the buoys, slowly, very slowly, but oh! so surely, that amorphous blob would get bigger.

After the mild panic attack at the NW Goodwin, I calmed down and sat back for a lengthy and hopefully very boring run into Pegwell Bay. The course being steered was roughly 280 degrees, magnetic or true, who knows? didn't make a lot of difference one way or the other. We were on a flood tide, pushing us north and the wind, a stiff force three, possibly more to the south now, was also pushing the yacht north. With one thing and another, Solo and I were probably moving faster sideways than forward. This was not a problem, it had all been worked into the calculation. Okay, so I had taken a wild stab in the dark and for the moment it was paying off.

All that was required of me was to keep the power station on the starboard bow, this could be one point, could be six points off the bow, as long as the cooling towers were on that side of the boat, I would be able to get home, relatively dry and with body and soul just about in one piece.

Twenty minutes onto my new course; there I was minding my own business, wondering when the hell things were going to start to get bigger. Scanning the horizon, keeping a good look out, as you're meant to, I espied another vessel chugging towards me. She was well down to the south and seemed to be moving fairly fast, but then compared to Solo, a tortoise with three wooden legs would be moving fast. I didn't take much notice.

Ten minutes went by: "Oh oh! What's going on here...?"

I decided to investigate a bit more closely as to what was occurring with this ship from the south. Using the ratchet winder on the port side as a bearing indicator, I suppose you'd call it, I eyed along it to this object. Obviously, a small coaster, a small coaster that was getting bigger by the second. I stood there for a minute, maybe a little more...

"Bloody Hell... This thing's on a steady bearing..." I was on a collision course!...

I couldn't believe it. Stuck out in the middle of nowhere, only two boats for miles and this floating piece of junk was going to run me down...

Don't panic... 'I'm a yacht, not under power, he's got to keep out of my way... Hasn't he?...'

I kept on checking the situation, using my improvised bearing indicator. Fifteen to twenty minutes later, the thing was still on a steady bearing and by this juncture roughly, only a mile away. It was around about then, that I began to feel more than a bit on the nervous side.

She was a small bulk carrier. When I say small, three, four thousand ton, a damn site bigger and heavier than my little boat. Also, she was chugging along at a fair old rate and this meant that she wasn't going to turn on six pence, or stop in a hurry, not that it showed any signs of either. The problem, then became, should I alter course, but if she decided to alter at the last minute and try to come around my stern, which is what she should have done, the situation would be even worse... "Oh sugar! This could get nasty..."

'Wait... maybe the coaster was in a narrow channel? Then I should be the give way vessel, Oh my God!'

About half a mile now... This rust bucket (and it was a rust bucket), was trundling along at eight knots or more... If something didn't happen soon, in five minutes, I was going to be just so much plastic and wood, not to mention flesh and bone, mashed up on the surface and that's if I was lucky.

I looked up at the bridge, couldn't see a soul... The correct procedure was to go hard a starboard, I would have had to gybe in a hurry and under pressure. Undoubtedly, I would have ended up moving closer to this hulk, and I was already too close. I pushed the tiller away from me and went to port...

The rules said something about making a bold manoeuvre, so that other vessels could readily see your intentions. Thirty degrees that was it, anymore and I would have stalled again. That wasn't going to happen. It was necessary to keep some way on, just in case this sod did try to turn... Did not trust this floating lump of metal at all. I had the distinct feeling, whether I was in the right or in the wrong the 'Andorea B' would have run me down regardless.

She went down my starboard side at a hundred yards distance, still couldn't see anyone on the bridge. I mouthed some obscenities at it anyway.

The only people I saw on her were a couple of oicks hanging onto the stern rail, sneaking a quiet fag. Needless to say, I didn't give them a wave...

I rode out the ship's wake, turned back to my original course and put it down to experience, a bad experience.

Surely that had to be the last. Mother nature had had a go at killing me. One way or another, I had had a go at killing myself and now some idiot in a four-thousand-ton floating scrap yard had had a go, that's assuming there had been someone on the bridge of the f'ing Andorea B.

I settled back to my old routine of keeping Richborough power station on the starboard bow. The wind had sprung up and maintaining a steady course was proving more awkward than it had been before. The bows were swinging around quite vigorously and due to this the sails were being sucked first one way then the other. It was all a bit ragged. Never mind, it was all part of the fun...

After a bit of messing around, steering ten degrees this way, then ten degrees that and playing with the sheets, I did manage to end up with something akin to a steady motion. However, in order to steady her up I was sailing with the wind on the port beam and it was a bit of a struggle to keep the old power station on that starboard bow. On several occasions, the towers wandered into the port side danger zone and not by just a little bit either.

The waves were causing the problem, rather than the wind. They were not particularly big, maybe two feet, but they were perky little buggers and every time they hit the port bow, the front end was thrust sideways. We were kind of snaking through the water. Not the most comfortable of rides. I have a sneaky suspicion that a true sailor would have loved every minute; suffice it to say I wasn't a true sailor...

As per usual there was a compromise between the desire to get from A to B as quick as possible and in my case, the desire just to get there.

I could have come off the wind and had an easier ride, probably been quicker, but it was more messing around. No doubt would have had to restarted the engine; the more messing about, the more there was to go wrong. No! The way I was sailing was getting me there and that would do for me.

Another coaster came into view; I checked its bearing... 'Good God not another one!' It was on a steady bearing. 'What the frig was going on...?' I stood amazed. This time I didn't have to worry; I was just panicking over nothing. As fortune would have it, this vessel, looked like an over grown barge, was slowly drawing ahead of me. I was becoming paranoid. In the end, it passed in front of me a good half mile off.

I may not have been in a massive rush, but time was getting on, it had been a long night and the day was turning out to be even longer. I had turned the corner at the NW Goodwin at 12.05 and an hour later my goal of the tall chimney and three cooling towers of Richborough power station did not appear to be getting any closer. This certainly wasn't due to the lack of wind. While I wasn't looking, it had notched itself up to a brisk force four, not quite a southerly, south by west more like. Every now and then the wind took the sails and Solo bent over with a bit of a jolt. If these little knockdowns had occurred twenty-four hours earlier, I would have freaked out, started ranting and raving and pulling my hair out trying to figure out if I was going to live or die. Then and there, I just brought the boat into the wind, so as to empty the sails and carried on.

The time did come to take more concerted action. These knock downs began to happen a little too often for comfort and although it would slow me down, I furled in the foresail.

The wind increased further and the sea became rougher, think I'd been here before. From sailing in reasonable conditions to pain in the arse conditions, took about half an hour. Then the first squall hit.

I could see it coming; it was miles to the south, a line of rain with very crumply sea beneath. This grey mass of swirling rain was heading right down my throat. I was going to get wet and blown around a little, so what's the big deal...? Twenty minutes later, when it finally engulfed me, it was like a shock wave crashing into the boat. It was a big deal...

The rainstorm began by whistling and howling in the rigging. I expected that, I didn't expect the knock down, it was a biggy... In a second... The mast went over forty-five degrees to the starboard and everything went with it, including me. I felt like I was in a hurricane. "What the Bloody Hell...!"

It was a lot more drastic than the gust of wind I was expecting. It would take more than an alteration of course to sort this mess out. The mainsail was flapping and cracking, tugging on the mast, causing all kinds of lurching movements. At the same time all sorts of weird, creaking and groaning noises were coming from who knows where...

I was safe enough at first, standing on the port side, gripping the handrail for all I was worth. Once I had recovered from the initial shock, I put the tiller over to bring the head into the wind, but that was having little or no effect, I had to pay out the mainsail and the only way I could do this was by letting go my grip on the handrail. I don't suppose I even thought about, it just had to be done... I let go the handrail and had to swap hands with the tiller, I was balancing at a very strange angle, I pulled the self-releasing clamp and let the main out, I even had some control over it. The boat came upright and sort of shook itself. The danger was over...

There was an awful lot of huffing and flapping from the sail and I also was getting a considerable soaking from the waves breaking over the side of the boat. However, it didn't take too long before I gained some semblance of control over the sail and although still being battered by a raging bull of a storm, things were almost back to normal.

Once inside the squall, it did not seem quite as bad. Of course, by then the sail had been trimmed and the yacht's heading modified to account for the conditions. There was no way you could say the experience was barrel of laughs, but as for the initial attack by the squall, that was something else, really frightening. You could see it coming, looked like a rain storm, didn't look anything.

When it came upon you though, it was like being run over by an express train. The ferocity, the sound and the speed at which it hit, it was incredible.

I thought I was learning about Mother Nature's little tricks, but this one caught me with my pants well and truly down. Fifteen minutes probably less and it was all over. Well, it was far from all over as I was soon to find out.

The wind was stronger than ever and a swell (another bleeding swell) had been stirred up by the squall, about three feet, nothing compared to the previous night, but it was on the beam and giving my yacht a bit of a hard time.

I gazed out to the north and west over Sandwich Bay; there were an awful lot of those white horses out there. The sea was very angry looking, not completely white, but it wasn't far away from it. Had to be a force five maybe as much as a six.

I cast my eyes over the mainsail. The sail was taking a bashing again and I knew something should be done about this before I was staring disaster in the face, yet once more. 'Reef the main,' that was the solution, but as I didn't know how to do this, I just said: "Sod it...!" (my favourite words of the day) and carried on.

A second squall came in. Again, I had plenty of time to prepare for it. At least I had an idea what to expect this time. Sure enough, Solo went over, I immediately slackened off the mainsail sheet to let the wind spill out and this solved any serious problem that may have occurred. We only went over about thirty degrees. It was sorted. I was totally blasé about the whole thing. I don't know if I was tired, fed up, distraught or what, just couldn't give a monkey's uncle.

I turned my face up to the looming, grey body of the cloud whirling over my head:

"Is that the best you can do!!!" I screamed at it... The whipping rain lashed into my face; I turned back to the job in hand...

The only crumb of comfort during this period was that my power station was finally beginning to get a little larger; it was painfully slow and it felt like I'd been on that course for hours on end. In point of fact, I had.

The B2 buoy had been visible for some time; it was the second buoy I had come across, on that heading at least. The B2 was a noisy one though: it had a bell. The bell was tolling constantly, which got on your nerves at times and was a comfort at others. I was alongside the dongs about two o'clock, just as another squall went through. This was to be my last squall and to be honest, I hardly noticed it.

The B2 buoy was south of Richborough. Despite all the southerly weather, I had managed to end up more or less where I wanted to be. It should have been an easy sail to get to the channel, with the wind abaft the beam, heading northwest. Another mile and I could lower the main, start the engine and head for the safety of the river. In this wind, I would be there in about two minutes.

It didn't take two minutes, fifteen or twenty more like. The problem wasn't that the boat didn't have enough speed, the problem was. I was lost!

The channel marking buoys were not easy to see, it was still fairly choppy out there and not having been there before, I simply didn't know where to look. As for my chart, if you wanted to call it that, it was less than useless. Not entirely true. This bit of parchment did indicate where not to go, which of course, was exactly where I was heading.

The whole thing became very confusing and in the end, I missed out part of the channel; cut the corner and went over the shallows. The depth sounder was on and the alarm for the one metre depth was buzzing away pretty nigh constantly. Every second I was expecting to hit the bottom. On this trip if something could go wrong, it would.

For once my luck was in. After only a few minutes of the annoying squeaks from the sounder, I made it through to the main channel. Strangely enough, with no unpleasant grating sounds from the underside of the yacht. Wonders would never cease.

I thought I would have been at least a little euphoric, arriving at the point I'd struggled so desperately, at times, to get to. I can only assume I must have been emotionally drained, didn't feel anything. All that was in my mind was to find somewhere safe and get that bloody sail down for the last and final time.

I sailed further into Pegwell Bay, making sure I was within the channel markers. The tide was well in, but still, I didn't want to take more risks than I had to. I'd taken too many of them over the past thirty hours as it was. If I had hit the bottom and got myself stuck, I might have been there for another twelve hours and I didn't think I could have taken that.

The wind and sea state were a lot calmer now I was well inside the bay. This was not to say that the wind had died away to nothing. Far from it, there were still some strong gusts coming through.

I had half hoped that I would get away with just drifting, while I lowered the sail, but this really wasn't an option. The amount of time it was going to take me to get the sail down and tie up, I would probably have been blown half way up the beach. I would have to drop the anchor.

It wasn't long, another ten minutes from the time I entered the channel, before I decided I had gone as far as it was safe to do so, with my forlorn sailing skills at least. I turned into the wind, ran forward and threw the anchor over.

'Was that it? Could I finally breathe a sigh of relief?'

Chapter Eight

The Final Chapter
(Pie and chips)

I was there for another twenty minutes, cursing and swearing at the mainsail. The wind was blowing it all over the place and taking me with it most of the time. Twice I had to grab onto something or other to stop myself from being tossed into the very choppy waters of Pegwell Bay. I was in a tremendous hurry, no reason for it, but I was rushing around like a man demented and the more I rushed, the more things went wrong.

Finally, I managed to sort myself out and the sail was down and wound up around the boom. As it happens, by the time I had finished the sail wasn't the only thing wound up.

I started the engine and went forward to bring up the anchor. As soon as the anchor was free of the bottom, we began to drift backwards and by the time I had managed to get the pick on deck, dash back to the cockpit and turn the revs up, we had drifted outside of the main channel.

As I moved out of the shallows, a grimace on my face, waiting for the bottom to scrape (I didn't like my bottom being scraped, strangely enough). Joking aside, if Solo managed to get lodged on a sandbank (and there were plenty around), I think I would have thrown myself overboard, just to get it all over with.

The weather in Pegwell Bay was a vast improvement on the conditions further out to sea, but still very gusty. The yacht's engine struggled to power her way towards the channel. We were steaming directly into the wind and the tide for that matter.

Eventually and with the poor old engine working its guts out, we crept past one of the buoys. Thankfully I turned to starboard. The wind and the tide would be with me now, it was going to be a breeze from here on in, no doubt it wouldn't be a 'gentle' breeze.

I steadied her up and headed for the river mouth.

The channel was well marked and more to the point, nice and wide. Even I could manage to steer between the various poles and buoys without getting into trouble. Well, so you would have thought. I had only been going for two minutes with the engine on and what happened? I ran aground... "You're f'in joking me!"

I wouldn't have minded, but I was inside the markers, only just it was true, but definitely inside.

This set back, as it happened, was not a real problem. The boat was still bobbing around and I guessed we had only just touched the mud. In fact, I used the grounding to my advantage. I had been in such a hurry to get the sail down and raising anchors and the like, that I'd forgotten to fill the petrol tank up. Being stuck in the shallow water made the boat that much more stable. This as good a time as any to rectify my minor oversight. The wind blew most of the petrol into the bay, but in the end, I had a full tank of gas. I clunked the gears in reverse and we came off as smooth as anything. Back in forward, revs up and aiming for the middle of the channel this time, Solo headed for the entrance to the river once more.

Twenty minutes later and we were in the river proper. Surely even I couldn't do Solo or myself any harm in the quiet waters of the Stour... We were safe!

I was frustrated, annoyed and upset about the whole experience, don't know why, just wasn't at all a happy little bunny. Nevertheless, I thought it only right to celebrate. Time for the last can of beer. I opened the can and sat back on the port side seat and thought back over the past day or so.

I just shook my head and took another gulp of beer.

As I was sailing up the river, there on the north bank was this old man pottering around with his boat – a clinker-built fishing boat. He was wearing a scruffy woollen jumper, a dirty old pair of jeans and rolled down wellies. He stopped what he was doing and looked at me...

'Jesus Christ! It's the same old guy I'd left at Oare Creek...' I was certain of it. The old man gave a node and maybe a smile... I nodded back... 'No! Couldn't be...'

And there you have it. If any proof was needed, I had gone over the edge and was now quite mad... I looked away, I actually said to myself: 'If I look back he'll be gone...' I turned, there was the old clinker-built fishing boat… It hadn't been touched in years…

Ignoring my insanity, I was just too tired for any of that. I motored past the power station. It was one of the few things I had come to rely on that day and it wasn't a grey, amorphous, blob anymore. I raised my can of beer to the chimneys and even managed a smile.

An hour later and Solo was alongside the quay at Sandwich. Even that had been a minor nightmare. I had to turn around to face the tide so as to berth up, and then phone someone to get the bridge opened. My actual berth was the other side of the bridge. On more than one occasion I nearly reversed into the reeds on the north bank. I did ram the wall on the quay at least once. All this in full view of a goodly number of people. No doubt they were wondering what the hell I was doing. They weren't the only ones... There had been a nice big space for me to get into, but due to all the messing around, I had drifted well past this. To make matters worse, the vessel was getting a bit too close to the road bridge for my liking. The solid, stone pillared road bridge. Solo (and her mast) were not going to fit under...

Unusually, and very luckily, there was another space nearer the bridge. Somebody shouted for me to throw him a rope, which I did gratefully. We squeezed into this space, which was only just big enough for the yacht to fit into. Fortunately, don't ask me how, I didn't hit any other boats. I hit everything else, mind you.

All tied up, everything made ship shape, sort of. The next thing should have been a good few pints down the old hatch, but I was just too shattered. As a clambered up the ladder, despite it being a rickety, rusty old thing and moving around in its bolt holes, I was only too pleased to be on it. I thanked the guy who helped with the rope and found the phone box on the quay.

As I was leaving the booth, this tall, young guy approached me.

"Hello there, you made it then..." he said cheerfully enough.

"Yea just about," I replied, not entirely sure who he was.

"We were getting a bit concerned, it's a bit blowy out there."

"You're telling me..."

Eventually, he explained he was with Sandwich Marine and had seen me arrive. His attention drawn, no doubt, by the gasps from my audience, as I single handedly destroyed Sandwich. Apparently, he thought he had better show me where to go, which was very nice of him really.

As I was about to go down the ladder to the yacht, a couple of friends I knew from the pub walked by.

"Just got in then, what's it like out there?" Andy shouted over.

"Windy" I said tersely, I just didn't want to talk to anyone, "About a force six..." I added, trying to sound a little less like a gorilla with a sore head.

"More like a force seven..." Andy countered, with a knowing look (he and his girlfriend also had a yacht) I looked at him, shook my head and disappeared down the ladder.

It wasn't long before the bridge was swung open. I started her up and managed to ease out of the space without too much damage to either boat or pride. My next problem, the bridge was astern of me... I was facing the wrong way. Shouldn't have been a problem, but with my piloting skills, I could feel a disaster of Titanic proportions looming large.

However, astoundingly as it happened, this time I came about in one easy manoeuvre. I had to go down river a hundred yards to give myself a bit of room, but just pushed the tiller hard over and round we went. I think I may even have fooled a few people into believing that I actually knew what I was doing. I sailed through the open bridge. The chap on the controls of the bridge, just looked at me as if I were mad and all things considered, maybe he was right.

Another two hundred yards and Steve, the guy from Sandwich Marine was waiting, I had to turn around yet again. 'Bloody pain in the backside this is...' But, I was getting the hang of it by now and again turned around in one, then simply eased Solo straight in the finger berths, as they were called. I managed all this, almost like I'd been doing it all my life. Steve stayed and helped me tie up, but after about five minutes made his excuses and left. I don't think I was overflowing with joy and laughter at that particular moment in time.

That was it, no beer, no recounting my epic, sorry saga to the pub locals... Caught the bus, although to this day I can't remember... Arrived home about half five in the afternoon...

"You're a bit late" the wife said, "was it fun?"

"I'm going to sell the bloody thing..."

"Oh good. It's pie and chips for tea..."

Chapter Nine

The Last Bit

I still go sailing from time to time and yes, I do enjoy it. Just pottering around Pegwell Bay and if I'm feeling daring I sometimes venture into Ramsgate harbour.

I don't go out on my own very often these days and when I do, I make sure I have my new radio and my mobile phone with me and I still know where that old kitchen knife is, just tucked inside the cabin entrance.

I have even mastered the art of tacking, most of the time that is. A wee bit of ballast in the front end was the secret, so simple when you know how. And maybe that is what it's all about: you can't just do stuff and hope for the best. Sometimes you will get away with it, like me on my little sailing trip. But sometimes you won't...

Sailing Solo as a hobby? Well, it has its good points, escaping the Monsters and the Dragon still has its appeal and maybe I have even learned a few things. Then again, it may be time for me to hang up my sails and take up something a little less stressful...

Mountain climbing is fun they tell me.

What could go wrong?

Review

If you enjoyed this book please leave a review.

Reviews are the life blood for authors and help circulation... That said, and more importantly, if this book makes just one budding sailor stop and think, my work is done.

sailingsoloalone@live.co.uk

Printed in Great Britain
by Amazon